New Technologies in
Exploration
Geophysics

Gulf Publishing Company
Book Division
Houston, London, Paris, Tokyo

New Technologies in
Exploration
Geophysics

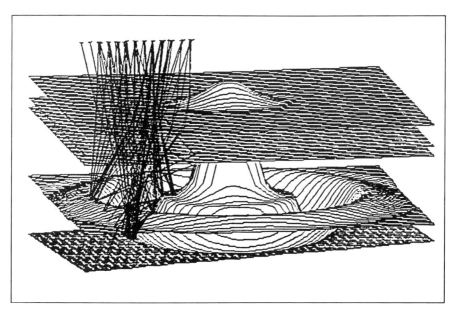

H. Roice Nelson, Jr.

New Technologies in
Exploration Geophysics

Copyright ©1983 by Gulf Publishing Company, Houston, Texas. All rights reserved. Printed in the United States of America. This book, or parts thereof, may not be reproduced in any form without permission of the publisher.

Library of Congress Cataloging in Publication Data

Nelson, H. Roice, 1949—
New technologies in exploration geophysics.
Includes bibliographical references and index.
1. Prospecting—Geophysical methods.
2. Geophysical instruments.
I. Title.

TN269.N38 1983   622'.15   82-21120
ISBN 0-87201-321-9

Cover photo is courtesy of Sierra Geophysics, Inc.

Acknowledgments

Many people have contributed to this book. Laura Pankonien was the key force in initiating, editing, and encouraging me to write the series of articles for *World Oil*, which are the basis of this book. Technical assistance from the literature, fellow scientists, vendors, and friends has been documented in the references.

There has also been tremendous help from the staff at the University of Houston's Allied Geophysical Laboratories, which started with a computer terminal and modem so I could write at home in the evenings, and expanded to having Shirley Bage correct the edited magazine article drafts. Dr. G. H. F. Gardner edited and provided valuable comments on Chapters 2, 3, 4 and 6; Dr. John McDonald also helped with Chapters 1 through 4; Dr. Anne Simpson was involved with the preface, Chapters 2, 7, and 9; Richard Verm assisted with Chapters 6, 8 and 10; Dr. Olin Johnson and Dr. Duane Pyle provided much of the material on vector processors for Chapter 5; Dr. Sam Uselton aided with information on computer graphics for Chapter 7; Julie Norris, Director of Sponsored Research for the University of Houston, provided background material for the last chapter; Dr. Bob Sheriff helped with the introductory chapter, and even used a "new technology" (a computer terminal at home connected to the AGL computer) to review it; and Barbara M. Murray, the AGL Project Administrator, R. G. (Rudy) Charest, the Research Computation Laboratory Manager of Operations, and Dr. K. K. Sekharan, the SAL manager, aided in numerous ways, specifically by helping me have time to write and edit.

The most important acknowledgment, to me, is to thank my family for support; especially for helping me find the time and quiet necessary to put this material together. My wife, Marti, read and provided valuable comments on most of the chapters, and kept our five children occupied while I was writing. Because Marti enjoys making our house a home, properly training our children (which I am confident is more valuable than anything I will be able to accomplish) and supporting me in professional and church work, I dedicate this book to her.

Contents

Preface ix

1 **Reflection Seismology: An Introduction** 1
Basic Theory. Acquisition. Processing. Interpretation. Summary.
References.

2 **Technological Trends** 61
Data Collection Techniques. Processing Technology. Interactive Interpretation. Change. Training Explorationists. Summary. References.

3 **Multi-Channel Seismic Recording Systems** 79
Why More Channels? Data Transmission. Multi-Channel Recording. Recording Systems. Summary. References.

4 **3D Seismic Techniques.** 95
3D Acquisition. Processing 3D Data Sets. 3D Interpretation. Summary.
References.

5 **Vector Computers.** 111
Scalar Computers. Vector Computers. Geophysical Applications. Summary. References.

6 **Numerical and Physical Modeling** 127
One-Dimensional Modeling. Two-Dimensional Modeling. Three-Dimensional Modeling. Summary. References.

7 **Interactive Computer Graphics** 159
Traditional Display Terminals. Color Raster Graphics. Image Processing.
Vector Refresh Graphics. Raster Vector Combinations. Future Graphics
Developments. Hardcopy. Graphics Justification. Summary. References.

8 True 3D Display Devices **187**
Parabolic Mirrors. Projection Imaging. 3D Displays from Film. Beam-Splitting Techniques. Rotating Light-Emitting Diodes. Vibrating Mirrors. Summary. References.

9 Interactive Interpretation **207**
Why Computerize? Computer Applications. Intelligent Picture Processors. Industry Presentations. Approaching Developments. Summary. References.

10 Managed Data Bases **231**
Why DBM? The Foundation of DBM. Structuring Storage. Exploration Applications. Satellite Data Transmission. Security. Summary. References.

11 Industry/University Exploration Training **251**
The Problems. Funding Research/Education. Needed Innovations. Summary. References.

Index **273**

Preface

The purpose of this book is to review the new technologies that are impacting oil and gas exploration now, and how they are expected to continue to do so. The title specifies exploration geophysics because the new technologies described apply to studying the earth using quantitative physical methods. This is the basic definition of geophysics. Although there are many disciplines covered by this definition, the most common is reflection seismology. Perhaps, a more correct title would be "New Technologies in Exploration Seismology," but the term seismology, in practice, is not as frequently used as geophysics.

The book is specifically written for oil exploration managers who find themselves removed from the new developments that are now influencing and will continue to affect their decisions. However, it does give a comprehensive overview of new technologies in each of the major areas of acquisition, processing, and interpretation of seismic data. Students, new geophysicists, and experienced explorationists who feel isolated from some part of the field will find this book a worthwhile review of those items that are expected to most affect their careers over at least the next decade.

There is an emphasis on changes in methods of seismic interpretation, mainly because most past developments have been in acquisition and processing. For the most part, seismic interpretation is still done with colored pencils, as in the 1950s. It is reasonable to project that there will be more changes in interpretation techniques than in either of the other areas over the rest of this decade. There have been important developments in the areas of direct

hydrocarbon detection (bright spot analysis) and seismic stratigraphy. However, these topics have been covered by other au-
thors. The emphasis of this book is on the anticipated effect of
interactive computer graphics on seismic interpretation. Another
reason for this emphasis is that most of my geophysical experience
has involved seismic interpretation.

The book is organized around the same steps that are used to
work with seismic data. These steps are learning the science,
collecting data, processing and modeling the data, computer handling and display of results, and finally integrating interpretations
in order to define the subsurface geology. Chapter 1 is an introduction that reviews the basic principles used in reflection seismology.
It is specifically for exploration managers who have come from
other fields and want to get a non-mathematical review of the
science their people use. Chapter 2 previews the technological
trends that are discussed in detail in the remainder of the book.
Acquisition developments are emphasized in Chapters 3 (telemetry and other large multi-channel acquisition systems) and 4 (3D or
areal seismic techniques). Seismic processing techniques are relatively more advanced than either of the other areas. The biggest
anticipated changes in processing, i.e., increased computation
speeds via hardware improvements and new numerical modeling
techniques, are reviewed in Chapters 5 and 6. The use of new
computer graphics hardware promises to have a major effect on
working with seismic data in all three application areas. Chapters 7
and 8 review developments in computer controlled methods of
displaying seismic data. Interpretation techniques, particularly
interactive interpretation techniques for integrated geophysical
interpretations, are analyzed in Chapters 9 and 10. The concluding
chapter discusses how universities and industry must work together in order to train the scientists needed to work with these
new technologies in exploration geophysics.

It is not the intention of this book to directly compare different
products or systems. There is no recommendation as to which of
any comparable systems is the best buy for any specific reason.
Throughout the book reference to company product names is
made simply as examples of the equipment under discussion. For
instance, there are hundreds of graphics hardware vendors, and
therefore the only mention is of those systems with which I am

somewhat familiar. No product endorsement is intended. In some cases, like Chapter 1 (an introduction to reflection seismology) and Chapter 6 (numerical and physical modeling), where the historical development of a subject is traced, some significant subjects and contributors will certainly have been missed. I apologize in advance. There will also be new developments that are not covered in this book, and if you, as a reader, have corrections or contributions in these areas, please forward them to me in care of the publisher for possible inclusion, with due credit, in future editions.

H. Roice Nelson, Jr.
Houston, Texas

CHAPTER 1

Reflection Seismology: An Introduction

The basic ideas behind using reflection seismology are as simple as properly using a mirror to see things that are not in front of you. This chapter introduces the concepts and key definitions behind seismic exploration. The material is divided into the logical subdivisions of basic theory, seismic data acquisition, processing, and interpretation. As a non-mathematical summary of the important principles behind this science, there will be many subjects that will be skimmed over or skipped altogether. However, the key intention is to provide a general foundation for the rest of the book without basing the information on graduate-level mathematics. This chapter is directed to those who have little knowledge of geophysics or want a basic review. This specifically includes executives from other backgrounds who are working with and interested in the science behind geophysical exploration for oil and gas, the problems geophysicists are attacking, as well as the relation of reflection seismology to the new technologies described in the remainder of the book.

The most common use of geophysics, by far, is to define subsurface geology in order to improve the probability of success in drilling for oil and gas (hydrocarbon deposits). However, there are many other applications for reflection seismology: mapping coal seams, locating geothermal prospects, defining near-surface geology for building foundations and road cuts, etc. A discussion of geophysics normally includes sections on gravity and magnetics measurements, electric induction methods, magnetotelluric use, seismic refraction, earthquake seismology, geochemical exploration, and Landsat imagery. The author in no way intends to minimize the importance of these other techniques by not including detailed descriptions of their use. The emphasis of this book is on reflection seismology. Although many of the new technologies discussed have across-the-board applications, the transfer to other areas of geophysics is left to the reader. This emphasis is largely due to the fact that over 95% of the expenditures in geophysics are in the area of reflection seismology. The percentage of geophysicists that work in this area of geophysics is similarly weighted. The tie to the oil and gas industry and the dependence of our society on energy is the obvious cause of this emphasis.

BASIC THEORY

Reflection seismology is the study of the reflection of seismic waves off of subsurface geologic interfaces. The underlying principle is as simple as measuring the depth of, for instance, a large diameter water well by measuring the time required for an echo to be reflected from the well bottom and knowing the velocity of the sound waves in air. Sound energy from an explosion or other artificial seismic source at the surface of the earth propagates only downward through a homogeneous earth. However, the velocity-density variations between different layers of geologic strata results in reflection of some of the seismic energy from the rock layer interfaces, in a manner similar to the sound echos. Reflection seismologists measure the two-way travel time of seismic energy from an artificial seismic source to these interfaces and back to the receivers.

The path of the seismic energy wavefront can be simplified by drawing raypaths, as shown in Figure 1-1. These raypaths comply to Snell's Law, which says that the angle of incidence equals the angle of reflection and the change in direction of refracted energy is predictable. The angle of incidence is the angle between the raypath and a line perpendicular to the geologic horizon. If the layer is horizontal or near horizontal, then the reflected energy returns to the surface of the earth where it can be measured and the travel time to the horizon determined. Sedimentary rocks were originally deposited as a series of nearly horizontal layers, though their attitude may have changed somewhat as a result of deformations since the time of deposition.

The process of sedimentary deposition has resulted in geologic layers with different physical properties and thicknesses. It is important to note that the sedimentary section is where hydrocarbons are trapped. Sequential layers are composed of a variety of materials that have been differentially compacted. The key properties that effect seismic waves are the velocity of sound waves in these layers and the density of the rocks. The product of the velocity and density of a geological layer is known as the *acoustic impedance*. At the boundary of two rock layers, with different acoustic impedances, some of the energy traveling downward in the top layer is reflected back to the surface, but most of the energy passes right on through the boundary, possibly being refracted (bent) in its direction as it travels on downward into deeper layers. This is illustrated in Figure 1-1A and B.

The amount of energy reflected upwards depends on the contrast in the acoustic impedances of the two rock layers. The ratio of the amplitude of the pressure reflected to the amplitude of the pressure incident to the boundary is called the *reflection coefficient* of that boundary.[1] The amplitude of the wave reflected is the acoustic impedance of the lower layer minus the acoustic impedance of the upper layer. The amplitude of the wave incident to the boundary is the sum of the two impedances. The reflection coefficients can be either positive or negative as shown in Figure 1-2. The magnitude of reflection coefficients for interfaces in the earth is typically between 0.001 and 0.1. It can be as high as 0.3 for seismic energy reflected from the sea bottom or a shallow gas sand.

The seismic energy that continues downward is refracted or bent in the same way light waves bend in water. When a wave crosses a boundary between two isotropic media, the wave changes direction such that the sine of the angle of incidence divided by the velocity in the first medium equals the sine of the angle of refraction divided by the velocity in the second medium. Because sedimentary rocks are normally deposited in layers that have increasing velocity and density, it should be fairly simple to use these basic principles to unravel subsurface geology.

However, sending, recording, and understanding seismic waves is complicated by several factors. The results are often not as straightforward as the preceding discussion implies. The earth can be a very complex medium for transmitting seismic waves. When an artificial seismic source starts the elastic wave system of the earth in motion, it can be very hard to recognize true reflections from the complex movement of the ground surface.[2] Seismic

(text continued on page 6)

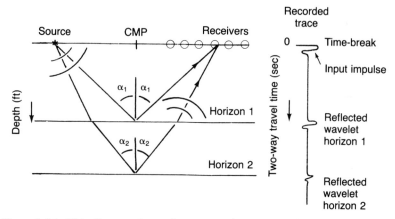

Figure 1-1A. This diagram shows the concept of common mid-point (CMP). Note that boundaries act as sources for new wavefront paths and that the angle of incidence equals the angle of reflection.

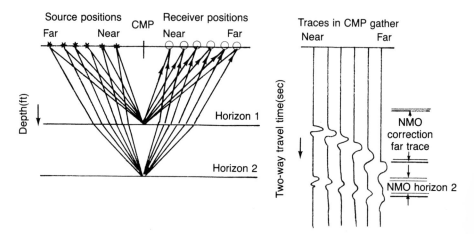

Figure 1-1B. In this CMP gather, reflections are recorded by six different sets of source/ receiver locations. The data is sorted into a CMP gather during processing. Dispersion, or the widening of the wavelet with offset, is exaggerated in the traces drawn on the right.

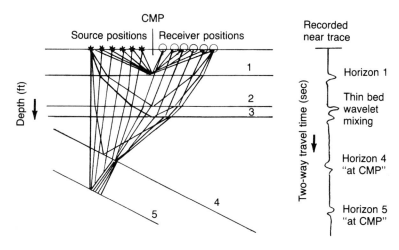

Figure 1-1C. A CMP gather over dipping beds shows one of the problems with the CMP method. Not only are the ray-traced reflection points at horizons 4 and 5 not located spatially at the CMP, but also note how the spatial locations of different source/receiver combinations move as a function of offset on horizon 5.

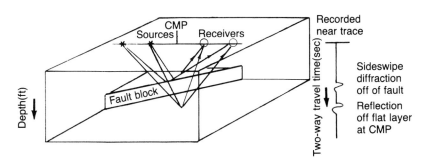

Figure 1-1D. Sideswipe reflections can come from steeply dipping layers. This example shows how diffractions from a fault block put out-of-plane events on a CMP trace.

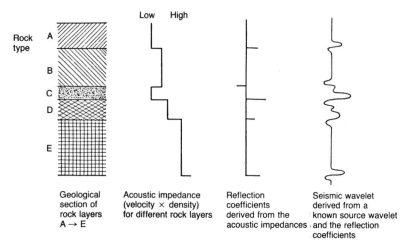

Figure 1-2. A generalization of the relationship between the geological column and seismic reflection coefficients. (After McDonald, Gardner, and Morris.[1])

sources are not pulse-like, the geologic boundaries are normally more gradational than abrupt, the reflection coefficients can be very small and the layers can be so thin that there is interference between reflections from the top and the bottom of the layers.[1]

Several basic assumptions are necessary to work with seismic data. One is that when a seismic source sends energy into the subsurface to be reflected back and recorded by a receiver, there is an important spatial location halfway between the source and receiver. This position represents the surface projection of where the data should be reflected from in the subsurface. It is traditionally called the common-depth-point (CDP), but will be referred to as the common-midpoint (CMP) in this book. The concept of CMP is illustrated in Figure 1-1. Note that the assumption of CMP location is true for flat pancake-like layers (Figure 1-1A and B), but does not hold if the layers dip (Figure 1-1C) or there are out-of-the-plane structures that cause sideswipe reflections (Figure 1-1D). Of course, most geologic horizons have dipping layers, are three-dimensional, and are surrounded by "sideswipe" seismic reflectors. This points out that the CMP assumption is not generally valid, however, it has proven to be the most successful acquisition and processing technique yet developed. Areal or three-dimensional (3D) seismic techniques are proving to further improve the seismic image of the subsurface.

The CMP method was originally suggested by Harry Mayne at Petty Geophysical Company about 1950 as a method to provide noise attenuation without also attenuating the reflection signal in an area of very severe noise problems. It subsequently became valuable in reducing energy multiply-reflected within the geological section. The CMP method is an acquisition and processing procedure that produces an interpretable vertical cross-section of subsurface geological strata. The data are collected using multiple seismic receivers for each seismic source position. The standard number of geophone groups in use for many years was 24, but a typical crew today has at least 96 on-line receiver stations for each source position. The receivers are normally located either in front, behind, or split on either side of the source along the seismic line (the road or trail that the seismic sources and receivers are moved along). Once the data are recorded for a specific source position, the live receiver stations are rolled-along (tailing receiver stations are dropped off and new stations brought on line in the lead). Seismic lines are linearly moved along in this manner by picking up geophones from receiver stations in the back and moving them to the front. On a land crew a receiver station is somewhat comparable to a plate on an army tank track rolling along.

The processing side of the CMP method starts by sorting CMP gathers (different source-receiver combinations that have the same CMP) similar to Figure 1-1B. There is a delay in the arrival of seismic events on increasingly distant traces (the reflection amplitude recorded in time as a "wiggle" or modified sine curve) in the same CMP gather. Simple geometry shows that traces with a farther source/receiver offset (distance between the source and the receiver) have a longer travel path than nearer offset traces traveling to the same subsurface reflection point. This delay in the arrival time of a reflection on traces with larger offsets can be corrected if the velocity that the seismic waves traveled to the reflector and back up to the receiver is known. The correction consists of lining-up in time or flattening reflection events on traces with different source-receiver offsets. This "flattening of events" on a CMP gather is known as normal moveout (NMO) correction. After this correction, these traces are summed, sample by sample, to give one stacked trace for each specific CMP. Because multiples (recorded seismic energy that does not come from a new geologic interface, but rather from bounces of the wavefront within a layer) do not have the correct velocities for the travel time for which they are recorded on the section, they do not flatten out during NMO correction. Statistically speaking, seismic events on the CMP gather, specifically noise, that are not additive on a majority of the CMP gathered traces tend to disappear after stack. This is why the CMP method increases the signal to noise ratio. There are problems with CMP stacking in the real world of 3D geology. Sideswipe (reflections from dipping layers out of the line of shooting) can alter the seismic reflections in the stacking process.

For marine CMP acquisition the receiver configuration is different in that the hydrophone streamer (with many receiver stations) is pulled along behind the boat. The shot spacing is a function of the firing rate and the speed of the boat, while the receiver spacing is a function of the hydrophone spacing in the cable. As in the land case, when CMP gathers are stacked, a good representation of the subsurface results. This is especially true if the data are collected along the direction that the geologic horizons dip. However, the CMP method will not solve problems created by out-of-the-plane or sideswipe reflections. Areal acquisition and processing are required to solve these problems (Chapter 4).

Another assumption is that the recorded wavelet is a simple reflection from each geologic horizon or boundary. There are several reasons why this is not the case. For instance, there are interbed multiple reflections and ghosts of the seismic energy. Huygen's Principle proposes that every point on an advancing wavefront can be regarded as the source of a secondary wave. This wavefront at a later time is the envelope (a line on a 2D wavefront cross-section or the surface of a 3D wavefront) that is tangent to all of these secondary waves. When this type of wavefront is evaluated in 3D, it is seen that reflections actually come from an area instead of a point. J. P. Woods' sparker model experiments empirically showed this.[3] He used a spark plug to create a sound wave in air that was reflected off of discs and rings of various sizes (see Chapter 6). Varying the size of the hole in the rings specifically showed that the area reflecting energy back is critical to the shape of the wavelet.

There are also three-dimensional variations of rock properties within different layers. The study of the elastic properties of rocks is much easier when one assumes that rocks are homogeneous and isotropic. This means that the rocks have the same properties throughout, no matter which direction the rock properties are measured in. However, this is not the case in nature. The source wavelet is continually being filtered by the earth as it travels to reflecting horizons and back to the surface. More often than not the reflecting geologic horizons are sufficiently close together that reflected wavelets interfere with each other to create a different wavelet shape than would result from a simple single-boundary reflection.[4] The study of these reflection patterns (resulting from depositional patterns) and of lateral variations in waveform, which indicate changes in the interference pattern as stratigraphy changes along the bedding, is known as seismic stratigraphy.[5,6]

A related factor is that seismic waves are elastic and not just acoustic. This means that there are transverse or shear waves (S-waves) transmitted in rocks, as well as compressional or pressure waves (P-waves). Compressional or acoustic P-waves are basically the same as sound waves. The expected P-wave response in the earth can be directly compared to or physically modeled by acoustic waves.[7] However, when shear and compressional waves are added, the resulting reflections from a simple model are very complex. This is illustrated in Figure 1-3, where a sequence of time snapshots of the elastic seismic energy are shown as they reflect off of a simple graben.[8] The shear waves (inner curves) travel at about one-half of the speed of the compressional waves (outer curves). Relating the S-wave and P-wave information has been shown to be useful in studying rock properties.[9] In order to obtain this separate information the proper field recording procedures must be followed.

Another example of the type of problems that exist in the basic assumptions used in reflection seismology is referred to as *dispersion*. It is normally assumed that when a seismic source is set off the wavefront is spherical and symmetric in all directions. This means that the wave shape in any direction out from the source should be the same. However, field records show that the wavelet being reflected from a specific horizon changes shape as a function of offset, the distance between the source and receiver. The distor-

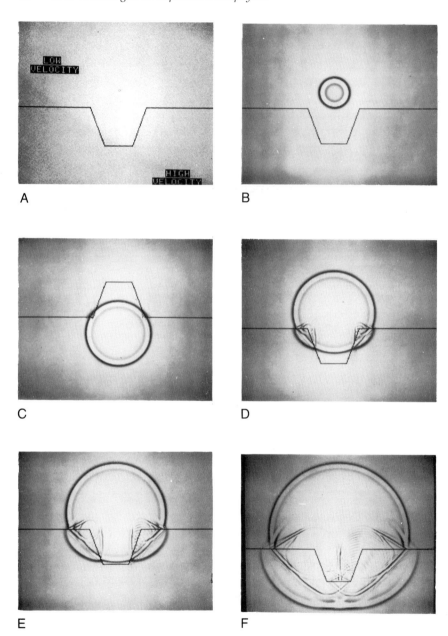

Figure 1-3. Time-elapse photos of vertical sections of a numerically derived elastic seismic wavefront. The outer circle represents the P-wave or compressional energy wavefront, and the inner circle is a converted shear wave (S-waves) front that travels about two thirds the speed of the P-wave. (After Kosloff and Reshef.[5])

tion is due to dispersion, interference effects from multiple-reflections, and changes in the reflection coefficient with offset. For example, a near offset trace might have a higher frequency pulse than the same reflector on a far offset trace. This wavelet stretching problem would seem to add to the other assumption problems that have been discussed and imply that reflection seismic techniques are not a good tool for energy exploration, especially when the costs of a seismic survey are compared to other geophysical techniques, such as gravity or magnetic surveys.

Then, why are these expensive and questionable surveys so common? The answer is simply because they work in helping to build an accurate picture of the subsurface geology. These surveys are also very cost effective when compared to the cost of a dry well. The key problem in oil and gas exploration is to locate geologic structures that trap hydrocarbons. The reflection seismic method was originally developed as a means of discovering large geological structures, such as anticlines. Hydrocarbons, being lighter than water, tend to be trapped in the top of local structural highs in porous layers (i.e., sand) that are overlaid by tight fine grain size geologic layers (i.e., shales). Figure 1-4 illustrates four of the typical type of traps that are sought with this technology.[10]

This hydrocarbon search often starts with a synthetic one-dimensional (1D) seismic trace, calculated from well logs. The only direct subsurface information an explorationist has is from the 1D information tied to the well hole. This information consists of either the cores and cuttings from drilling or a series of measurements (well logs) that are made by pulling various instruments up the well hole. These well logging tools measure parameters like sonic velocity, density, electrical resistance, etc. Seismic data allows this 1D information to be expanded along a line in the form of two-dimensional (2D) seismic sections, or over an area in the form of a grid of seismic lines. Disregarding 3D effects, this is like using a giant knife to cut the earth in order to understand the subsurface. If 3D seismic techniques are used, the data will cover an area and a 3D volume of data will be available for processing and interpretation. The bottom line is to define the geology of the subsurface and accurately predict what the drill bit will find.

The history of seismic exploration shows a continuous struggle to improve the science and the techniques that are used in order to

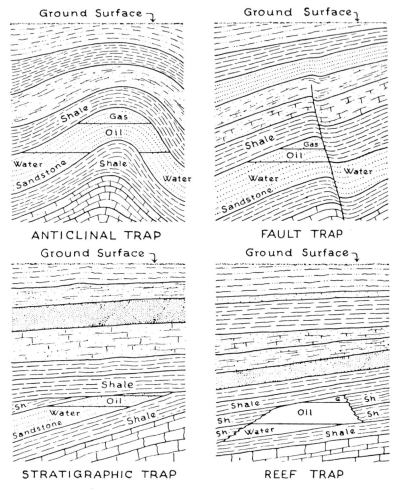

Figure 1-4. Typical examples of hydrocarbon traps. (After Dix.[10])

define the best possible drilling location as accurately and as quickly as possible. The history of how this science developed has been covered in several places.[2,11,12] Table 1-1 summarizes key historical events that can be defined by the public introduction of technologies to the industry. This table is based on charts in the book *Exploration Seismology*,[11] conversations with several geophysicists, and the author's experience. The dates are approximate because secrecy and competition often has resulted in the development and use of similar systems and procedures without public disclosure.

It is interesting to note some trends in the introduction of these technologies to exploration geophysics. The introduction of a major advance in acquisition has had a fairly direct relation to later developments in processing and interpretation. Five of these relations are underlined on Table 1-1. Note that the lead time to develop an interpretation procedure after a field technique was developed has dropped from 19 years to 7 years.

Another interesting trend, which does not show up on the table, is the change that has occurred in seismic contractor activity.[13] An early responsibility of seismic contractors was to provide the human "computer" to do an interpretation in the field. As time passed, the large oil companies developed their own in-house interpretation staffs, although small companies still rely heavily on outsiders, now mainly consultants rather than geophysical contractors. When digital recording was introduced, the seismic contractors started doing the processing of seismic data. This activity is presently undergoing change in that companies are realizing the importance of doing the processing in-house in order to ensure proprietorship and accuracy. This and the trend towards collecting more and more data, like in 3D surveys, leads to the conclusion that the major role of the seismic contractor over the next 15 years will be in seismic data acquisition and, specifically, 3D acquisition. There will also be much growth in companies that provide computers for processing 3D surveys and interactive interpretation systems to the oil industry.

ACQUISITION

Seismic acquisition systems consist of three basic subsystems: the energy source, the energy receiving unit, and the digital recording system. These subsystems are of equal importance in recording accurate, reflected seismic information. However, there has been much more development of and study in the source and recording instrumentation areas than on the effect of the units receiving the seismic energy. The basics in each of these areas are described in this section.

(text continued on page 19)

Table 1-1*
The Introduction of Technologies in Exploration Geophysics

	Acquisition	Processing	Interpretation
1910			
	1914 Minitrops mechanical seismograph.		
	1917 Fessenden patent on seismic method.		
1920			
	1921 Seismic reflection work by Geological Engineering Company.		
			1923 D and S Petty measured 2 events, 1 through & 1 around a salt dome.
	1925 Refraction for salt domes and other high velocity structures (Mexican reefs):		1925 "Interpretation" by spying on where other crews working.
	—40–250 lbs. dynamite per shot		
	—1 shot each morning when air calm		
	—Radio for communication and/or time break		
	1926 Refractions correlated for		

Table 1-1 continued.

Acquisition		Processing		Interpretation	
1930					
1931	Use of uphole phone. Truck mounted drills.				
		1932	Automatic Gain Control. Interchangable analog filters.		
1933	Use of multiple geophones per group.				
1936	Rieber sonograph, first reproducible recording.				
				1939	Started using "closed loops" to check misties.
1940					
		1942	Record sections.	1942	Spliced paper records.
1944	Large scale marine surveying.				
1950	Harry Maynes experiments with CDP method.			1950s	Human "computer" picked records in field & hand plotted cross-sectioning.
		1951–56	MIT GAG Group (Geophysical Analysis Group). Beginning of digital processing and time series analysis.		
1952	Analog magnetic recording.				
1953	First Vibroseis™ recording. Weight-drop recording.	1953	Analog Vibroseis™ correlation.		

* The shaded areas show how the time to develop an interpretation procedure lags behind new field acquisition techniques.

table continued on next page

Table 1-1 continued.

Acquisition	Processing	Interpretation
		1954 Gulf, Shell and V. Reynolds removed NMO & statics shift and recorded seismic data in variable density.
		1960s Interpretation centralized & moved out of field.
	1956 Central Data Processing Analog mag tape filtering, mixing (stacking), and record sections.	
1960	1961 Analog deconvolution and velocity filtering.	
1963 Digital data recording.		
1965 Airgun seismic sources.		
1967 Depth controllers on marine streamers.	1968 Maturing of digital seismic processing packages.	
1969 Shear wave crews. Introduction of VSP. 48–96 channel DFS-III standard recording system.		
1970	1970 2D migration for spatial reorientation.	

Table 1-1 continued.

Acquisition	Processing	Interpretation
		1972 Shell, Mobil, and Russians, Bright Spot or direct hydrocarbon indicators.
		1973 Anstey, batch display of color sections based on complex trace analysis.
1974 Sam Allen showed sign-bit recording useable.		
		1975 Chevron, Exxon, and Conoco seismic stratigraphy seminar.
1976 Gulf and GSI 3D seismic survey using telemetry systems.	1976 3D migration for true "focusing" of seismic events.	
1977 Gus Manufacturing introduced real-time Demux system.		1977 Lindseth—seismic log inversion. Reconstructing reflectivity equation for acoustic impedence.
	1979 Interactive processing parameter selection.	1979 Geosource Geostar data base management system.
1980	1980 Digicon, SSC, Litton VAX processing systems.	
		1981 Interactive computer graphics for seismic interpretation.

* The shaded areas show how the time to develop an interpretation procedure lags behind new field acquisition techniques.

table continued on next page

Table 1-1 continued.

Acquisition	Processing	Interpretation
1982 Digicon, Secure satellite transmission of marine seismic data during collection. Geosource, interactive 3D acquisition design.	1982 Cyber-200 and Cray-1 class vector processors introduced to seismic processing shops.	1982 Color computer graphics display seismic trace attributes.
		1983 Interactive 3D interpretation workstations.
1985	1985	1985
19? Fiberoptics transmission, eight 16-bit 1024 recording stations.	19? 3D migration before stack on vector processors.	19? Effective data base management systems.
19? Real-time cross-correlation, Demux and output in SEG-Y format onto 2 gigabyte optical disc storage or by satellite to a processing center.	19? Correct problems with assumptions: —CMP —Stability of signal (i.e., wavelet shape constant over data analysis window)	19? Time-sharing networks available to interpreters.
		19? Pattern-recognition and geological image processing.
19? Drilling noise evaluated to "see" in front of drillbit.	19? Autocorrelation over long enough window to counter continual earth filtering of the seismic wavelet.	19? Artificial intelligence.
19? Better ground-geophone coupling including 3-component phones in standard use.		19? Computer controlled data reduction.
2000		

* The shaded areas show how the time to develop an interpretation procedure lags behind new field acquisition techniques,

An *artificial energy source* for the seismic waves starts the procedure for acquiring exploration seismic data. This has traditionally been dynamite. In the 1920s, a standard shot hole would have from 40 to 250 pounds of dynamite in it.[14] Most early seismic surveys were carried out with shot-hole crews. Each source position had a hole drilled and the dynamite was put down the hole to get a better coupling with the earth, as well as to get under the weathering zone—unconsolidated near-surface rocks. (The tailing piles from the drill holes resulted in a sobriquet for the people working on seismic crews. In the southwestern U.S. there is a predatory insect called the "ant lion" that digs a pit in the sand, which looks like a small drill hole, and then waits for an ant or other insect to fall into the trap. These insects are also known as "doodlebugs," and the name "doodlebugger" has stuck in applying to anyone working in exploration seismology.)

Recent studies have shown that smaller amounts of explosives are sufficient to get good reflected signals.[15] There are numerous other methods of using explosive seismic sources. These include small charges in shallow holes, surface placed explosive packs, and air shooting. Surface shooting can have a temporary environmental effect (Figure 1-5A). Shallow hole shooting tends to affect agricultural areas less than other land seismic sources (Figure 1-5B). Air shooting, also known as the Poulter method,[16] involves placing explosive charges on stakes or poles so that the explosive shock wavefront is distributed over more ground surface than other impulse seismic sources. Primacord, a rope-like explosive, is also used as a linear seismic source, either on the surface, buried, or to set off explosive packs. When seismic work moved offshore, dynamite also moved with it. However, the introduction of air guns in the 1960s has resulted in dynamite seldom being used as a seismic source offshore today. Giving up dynamite offshore was to get away from bubble effects, because explosives couldn't be safely fired fast enough for the CMP method, as well as to solve environmental problems, like the number of fish killed.

Air guns inject a bubble of highly compressed air into the water, which is intended to be an impulse seismic source. However, the bubble oscillates as it alternately expands and contracts in rising to the surface. This complex source wavelet shape is simplified with a waveshape kit. The waveshape kit bleeds air into an expanding bubble to increase the pressure in the bubble during collapse. This

A

B

C

Figure 1-5. Typical land crew operations in southwestern Utah. (A) Surface shooting using ten 5-lb sacks of explosives on a primachord string. The environmental damage is temporary, but overshooting, like overgrazing, can cause long-term problems. (B) Shallow hole shooting of, say, 10 lbs of dynamite per shotpoint is better in agricultural areas. (C) The most common land seismic source is Vibroseis.^{TM} Normally, four of these trucks vibrate in synchronization.

reduces the sharpness of the bubble collapse and simplifies the source waveform.[17] There are many variations of marine seismic sources including Aquapulse™ (Western Geophysical), Vapor-choc™ (CGG), Maxipulse,™ water guns, sparkers, etc.[18]

In 1953, two other land sources were first tested, i.e., Vibroseis™ and weight drops. Weight drops are impulsive sources. An impulsive source consists of a spike of energy that contains all of the seismic wave frequencies transmitted in the earth. A modern example of this type of source is the "Betsy," a small one-man shotgun seismic source.

Vibroseis,™ on the other hand, puts a specific range of frequencies into the earth. The weight of a large truck or tractor is centered on a flat plate that can be vibrated over the range of seismic wave frequencies (Figure 1-5C). The unit is moved to a shot point location, where the plate is lowered to lift most of the truck weight off of the ground. A radio signal is sent to the recording truck to automatically switch on the recording instruments, and the plate is vibrated for, say, 12 seconds over a sweep of frequencies that range from, for instance, 10 to 60 cycles/second (hertz, Hz). The magnetic recording starts at the same millisecond the pad starts the vibration sweep (chirp), but will continue for, say, five seconds after the sweep stops.

A Vibroseis™ crew normally consists of four vibrator trucks and a backup maintenance truck. The trucks vibrate the ground in synchronization, for example, 16 times at equal move-up intervals over, say, a 330-foot source interval. The four simultaneous sweeps are combined in the earth. Sweeps from the 16 move-ups are summed in the recording truck for each recording channel. For a seismic line only five miles in length, these numbers imply that a vibration sweep is input into the earth more than 5,000 times.

The raw Vibroseis™ data are uninterpretable, because each reflecting horizon echoes the 12-second source sweep. The recorded wavelet is the combination of all of these overlain reflections. Reflection energy spikes for each subsurface horizon are generated in preprocessing using a mathematical procedure called Vibroseis™ correlation. The idea behind this is that the input sweep, which is known, is matched to the recorded wavelet at each time sample. This cross-correlation or matched filtering makes a spiked wavelet out of the 12-second sweep reflections from each reflector so that the wavelets look like data collected with an impulse source. Vibroseis™ has become a very common land seismic source. This is partly due to the fact that there is little environmental damage.

One Vibroseis™ technique that does damage the environment somewhat is shear-wave Vibroseis.™ The idea is to input transverse seismic waves into the earth with the source, and then record only the reflected shear energy. To accomplish this, special units are used that vibrate from side to side instead of up and down. This damages the environment because extra coupling is needed between the vibrating plate and the ground in order to generate transverse waves in the earth. The coupling consists of four upside-down pyramids on the vibrating plate that are worked down into the ground with a preliminary sweep. When a set of 4 vibrators makes 16 sweeps every 330 feet, the surface along the seismic line tends to end up like a newly plowed field. When good quality shear wave seismic data is used in conjunction with compressional data along the same lines, additional information can be determined about the actual rock properties of various geologic horizons.[9] This is still a relatively new, and some say unproven, exploration technique.

The *seismic energy receivers* are the second major component of a seismic acquisition system. These systems consist of geophones (jugs) on land and hydrophones for seismic acquisition on lakes or in the ocean. The geophone is typically a motion sensitive instrument. It consists of a magnet that is free to move along one axis (normally the vertical or P-wave axis) within a wire coil and the surrounding casing. The casing is connected to the ground by a spike that is normally about five inches long.

When the surface of the earth is moved by the elastic motion of seismic reflections, the geophone case also moves. The motion starts at the surface with an artificial seismic source, reflects off of subsurface geologic strata, then goes back to the surface. Although the geophone case moves, the magnet tends to stay stationary, and the movement of the coil/case creates an electrical impulse that is transmitted to the recording truck. There are special geophones that only measure transverse motion for use on shear wave Vibroseis™ crews. It is critical that these geophones be planted correctly, specifically properly lined up vertically. A typical geophone string consists of 12 to 48 jugs that are electrically connected in series. This means that the response from each geophone receiver group is electrically summed in the field. The geophones at each receiver position are normally laid out in an array. These arrays are specific patterns that help reduce some seismic noise.

An example of seismic noise is the air wave that is created by a surface explosion. When the seismic source activates, there is also energy transmitted into the air. This energy travels just above the surface of the earth at the speed of sound in air (1,130 ft/sec or slightly less) and moves the geophones. There is also energy that travels more-or-less directly from the source to the geophones through the earth's near-surface. This noise is the various forms of ground roll or surface seismic waves, and is fairly unique to each geographical area.

When a land crew first moves into a new area, there are often a series of tests to determine the best recording parameters to reduce this type of seismic noise, including receiver spacing and the type of array for the geophones at each station (source spacing and source arrays have a similar effect). Figure 1-6 illustrates the kind of data that can come from a noise survey. In the examples shown there were two sets of geophones laid out next to each other at 12 separate receiver stations. One set had a string of 24 geophones "potted" or planted within an area 1 foot in diameter at each receiver station. The other set had 48 geophones spread out with equal spacing over 330 feet (100 meters). The receiver stations were spaced 60 feet (18 meters) apart over a total of 660 feet (200 meters). Then two vibrators were placed side by side (so there was no in-line source array affect) and moved out 720 feet (220 meters) between source stations. A noise test determines the wavelengths of the noise waves that travel from the source directly along the receiver line with the grouped geophones. The receivers that are in an array are simultaneously recorded on different channels to see how well different receiver arrays attenuate the noise waves. Example air waves, surface waves, and reflections are shown in Figure 1-6A. In this case the receiver arrays that had 48 geophones equally spaced over 330 feet (100 meters) did a very good job of attenuation, as is illustrated in Figure 1-6B.

One of the least studied and biggest problems with land seismic acquisition is the coupling between the geophone and the earth. This can either be due to the different types of medium the geophone is placed in (sand, clay, bushes, rock, mud, ice, etc.) or

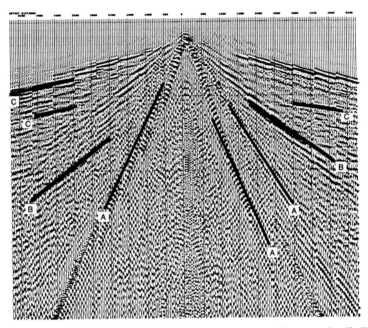

Figure 1-6A. A noise survey showing example air waves (A), ground roll (B), and reflections (C). The receivers were grouped at each of 12 receiver stations and the vibrators moved out to 8 source positions in each direction.

to the geophone placement engineer (jug hustler). In the U.S. a typical jug crew consists of about 20 people. The work is hard and usually over rough terrain, so there tends to be a high turnover rate of personnel. One result it that it is not uncommon to find geophones planted sideways or not properly connected to the cable. This is why it is so important to have good quality control in the field. It can make the difference between data and no data.

There is also a lot of room to develop newer and more versatile seismic receivers than the standard geophone. One exception to the lack of work in developing an improved geophone was presented at the EAEG Convention (European Association of Exploration Geophysicists) in 1982.[19] The geophone is a 0.6-ounce (17 grams), acceleration-sensitive transducer that gives good ground coupling and partial correction for the increased damping in the earth with increasing frequencies. The geophone uses internal electronics for a magnetodynamic velocity-nulling feedback system. This electronic feedback loop results in a geophone with

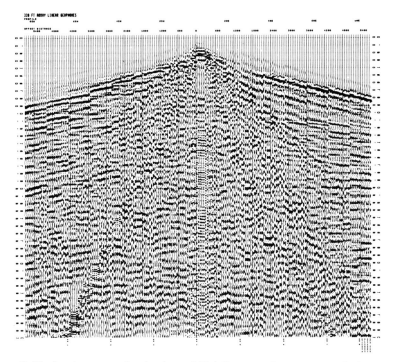

Figure 1-6B. A noise survey showing how a 330-ft linear receiver array cancels the strong air wave and ground roll. This same procedure can be done in processing if receiver stations are close enough together.

characteristics independent of the suspension orientation. New equipment like this might be a partial answer to improving data quality. However, a more complete answer might be economic, i.e., paying jug hustlers and field supervisors enough so they will stay with a seismic crew.

Offshore acquisition is very similar to onshore. Hydrophones record pressure variations rather than motion. They normally consist of a piezoelectric element that converts changes in pressure into electrical impulses, which are transmitted to the recording unit. The typical marine crew has a cable with 100 pairs of wires running to the same number of hydrophone arrays. The procedure is very similar to land, except for a few differences: the cable is dragged behind the boat; sharks chew on the cable instead of cattle and rats; and instead of trucks breaking wires by running over the cable, the cable gets caught or cut off in shrimpers nets (fairly rare). The biggest difference is that marine operations are completely handled from the boat, while a land crew has people all up and down the seismic line.

The coupling between the hydrophones and the water is much more consistent than on land. This is why relative seismic reflection amplitude studies are much more successful offshore. Consistent depth of the pressure sensitive hydrophones can be a problem. This is normally controlled with remote "birds" attached to the cable. The lateral movement of the cable by cross-currents can also be critical in accurate spatial location of seismic traces. This can be continuously monitored with digital compasses in the cable.

The location of the receiver stations in relation to the source positions determines the type of field configuration being used. As has been described, the typical procedure is to move the receivers along the shooting line to create a CMP section. However, there are many variations. For example, in marine shooting there might be a strong cross-current in the direction of shooting. This results in a feathering of the hydrophone cable and a swath of CMP's. This same areal coverage of CMP positions can be accomplished on land by shooting into receiver locations that do not line up along a specific line. These all simplify to the T-Spread described in Chapter 4, and include L-shooting, loop shooting, cross-spread shooting, and wide line profiling. The result of this type of source/ receiver configuration is that the CMP locations cover an area, instead of just a line.

There are also seismic acquisition configurations tied to boreholes. An early example that is still widely used is called "check shot" shooting. A geophone is lowered down a hole and the average velocity is determined as a function of depth by firing a series of shots on the surface in shotholes. An expansion of this technique is known as VSP-shooting or vertical seismic profiling. The general idea is to take advantage of the borehole to record seismic information inside the earth instead of only on the surface. The fundamentals of the VSP method have been around for some time and have been described in detail, first in the Russian literature.[20] As areal seismic methods become more widespread, they are being tied into VSP studies. It is reasonable to project that several geophone stations could be placed around an offshore platform, then when drilling pipe is replaced and the drill stem thumps against the bottom of the hole, the seismic response can be measured. This procedure has the potential of allowing the driller to "see" with seismic data in front of the drill bit.

The *recording unit* is the last major component of an acquisition system. Traditional recording systems bring a pair of wires from each receiver station into the instrument truck (doghouse) in parallel. The signal from each pair of wires is run through a roll-along switch, an analog preamplifier, and a frequency filter before it is digitized and put out on magnetic tape. In the case of Vibroseis™, the signal is put through a stacking box and then the summed sweep from each source position is transferred to tape. There is also a convolver box in the recording truck so that about every tenth shotpoint can be correlated in the field to ensure reasonable data quality.

The recording truck is run by an observer, who controls the activities of the entire recording crew in the field. For portable crews, which work in areas where trucks can't go, this includes coordinating the movement of geophones from the back to the front of the line via helicopter or horse, as well as moving up the master recording instruments. The observer also keeps a log or observer sheet describing everything that happens at each shot. This includes recording parameters like Vibroseis™ sweep range and filter settings, as well as remarks about what is happening on the line. For instance, on land several shots might have been skipped because they were too close to a water well or a house. On a marine crew there might be another boat in the area, or bad weather caused high seas. The observer also makes paper monitors of the recorded information at regular source intervals, and sends them into the processing shop with the data tapes. Normally, these paper records are from a camera unit that records the analog signals from 48 or 96 receiver stations with light deflected by galvanometers on light sensitive paper. There are a few recording systems that use high resolution computer graphics to display field records from buffered digital storage or from magnetic tape, rather than using these more conventional cameras for a quality check of the field records.

Chapter 3 discusses how many recording systems are moving much of this electronic equipment into the field as distributed subunits. The data from all of the recording channels is then brought into the recording truck serially using telemetry techniques. This greatly reduces the amount of wire that needs to be laid out to connect the receiver stations with the recording truck. A typical 96-channel crew has many cables with 100 pairs of wires in each cable and take-outs in which to plug a geophone string every

110 feet (the weight for a cable is about 85 pounds). Wire-line telemetry systems have 2-pair wire, like common television antenna wire, between each distributed recording unit and the controlling system. This kind of cable costs much less, and is easier to lay and fix in the field. In the case of radio telemetry units or remote cassette units there is no wire connecting the remote recording units. Distributed subunits are also being developed to work in parallel using fiber optics to transmit data at full resolution from thousands of channels simultaneously.

The activities of a 1983 seismic crew have many varied and complicated parts. However, the concept of a source, receiver, and recording unit is still basically the same as it was in 1940 (Figure 1-7). The differences are mostly in the types of support functions and

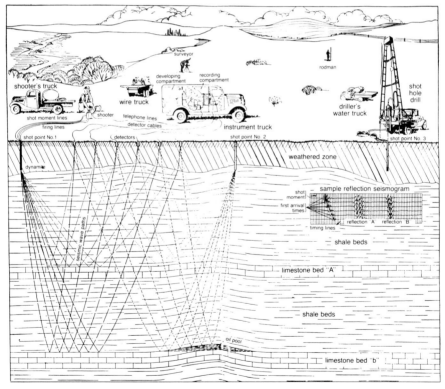

Figure 1-7. This diagram of a 1940s seismic shothole crew reflects the same basic configuration used today, except crews now use many more channels, various seismic sources, and sophisticated instrumentation. (After Nettleton.[2])

instrumentation that are available today. For instance, in addition to using a transit or an alidade to locate source and receiver stations, surveyors now use electronic distance measuring devices and portable satellite point positioning units. Shothole crews are less common, but still in use. In very rugged areas horses are still the best way to move the line along. Helicopters are used on some portable crews. The instrumentation in recording trucks has become miniaturized and much more sophisticated with new developments in computer technology and electronics. A basic difference is that there is a lot less down time on crews with modern equipment. There are several marine seismic operations that have a complete seismic processing system on board, along with a staff of processing geophysicists. But, there still must be permit agents, to get permission from the landowners to run a seismic line across their property; Vibroseis™ and air gun mechanics; cable and receiver (geophone and hydrophone) maintenance people; ship captains and cooks; electrical engineers to maintain the recording instruments; quality control geophysicists; and of course the party manager to make sure the operation runs smoothly. In fact, most seismic crews have these people plus about a third more in order to keep the crew running while some of the crew are on break.

Crew cost is one of the best indicators of the magnitude of seismic crew activity. In late 1982, a major seismic contractor was running land shot crews in the U.S. with 10–12 people and 100–160 people in Saudi Arabia, where labor costs make the use of huge receiver arrays needed for good data collection economically feasible. A major oil company runs each company seismic crew with from 20 to 28 professionals and about 20 temporaries. The cost per crew is between $230,000 and $400,000 each month. The same company's marine crew costs between $900,000 and $1,000,000 each month with a crew of 40 on the ship at one time. A contractor ship would typically be run with a crew of 12–18. Table 1-2 summarizes the average worldwide costs of seismic acquisition by survey type and method.[21]

PROCESSING

Advances in seismic processing have moved far faster than advances in acquisition techniques during the last 15 years. The

Table 1-2[21]
Worldwide Average Unit Costs by Survey Objective, Type, and Method (1981)

Survey Objective, Type, and Method	Total Crew-Months or Man-Months	Line-Miles or No. of Stations	Acquisition Costs (US$)	Average Coverage/Month or Man-Months	Average Cost/Month or Man-Months	Average Cost/Mile or No. of Stations
Petroleum						
Land						
Seismic (P-wave)						
Dynamite	5,158.3	254,745	1,333,010,875	49	258,420	5,232
Compressed air	111.4	20,354	34,982,988	182	314,030	1,718
Gas exploder	75.6	3,404	12,796,355	45	169,263	3,759
Weight drop	160.1	15,477	38,030,556	96	237,542	2,457
Solid chemical	87.0	9,400	38,420,000	108	441,609	4,087
Vibratory	3,674.3	224,565	844,096,234	61	229,729	3,758
Other	65.2	2,072	11,237,526	31	172,354	5,423
Seismic (S-wave)						
Dynamite	183.2	9,388	41,500,000	51	226,528	4,420
Compressed air	12.0	382	1,300,000	31	108,333	3,403
Vibratory	50.0	3,111	12,168,371	62	243,367	3,911
Marine						
Seismic (P-wave)						
Compressed air	701.1	664,232	418,523,218	947	596,952	630
Electrical	7.2	7,800	2,260,000	1,083	313,888	289
Gas exploder	282.7	199,693	114,389,675	706	404,632	572
Implosive	99.6	64,920	42,159,850	651	423,291	649
Solid chemical	32.0	25,600	14,080,000	800	440,000	550
Other	12.0	25,159	5,705,000	2,096	475,416	226

* Total includes government and university activity.

most significant development has been the widespread use of digital seismic recording and the advent of the digital computer. Exploration seismology was a major factor in the development of the basic algorithms that resulted in the computer revolution. In 1953, Professors R. R. Shrock and P. M. Hurley at the MIT Department of Geology and Geophysics formed an industry sponsored research group known as the Geophysical Analysis Group (the GAG group). Some twenty companies participated in the program, which was carried on under the leadership of Enders A. Robinson and Anne L. Simpson. The idea was to study how the digitization of continuous-time data could be used to repace the proliferation of specialized analog devices for solving individual geophysical problems. It was called time series analysis and allowed the recently developed computer to be used for a broad class of geophysical processing procedures. The June 1967 *Geophysics* summarizes the developments of the GAG group.[22] Although few of the developments reported in this volume were commercially implemented before the GAG group broke up in 1957, they did lay the groundwork for modern digital seismic processing.

As a result of the developments in digital seismic processing, any readable seismic data tape can be reprocessed and replotted to generate a new version of a seismic section. However, it is important to remember that if there were problems with the acquisition, the data can not be recovered and has to be recollected. The steps that are followed in processing seismic data have become fairly standardized, and an experienced seismic processor can generate reasonable data using "cookbook" procedures.

Figure 1-8 is a flow diagram of the normal processing steps used to preprocess and composite field data into a stacked seismic section. In order to initiate neophytes into seismic processing, the basic purposes behind the following twelve processing steps will be summarized: demux, Vibroseis™ correlation, CMP gather, decon, mute, velocity analysis, NMO correction, stacking, static corrections, spherical divergence corrections, filtering, and migration.

In order to compare similar quantities, a seismic trace is arbitrarily defined as having 2,000 samples at a 2 ms (millisecond) sample rate. A CMP gather is likewise defined as having 48 traces. The final parameter is a seismic line, which is defined as having 300 traces. Each sample consists of a 16-bit integer word. A bit is the

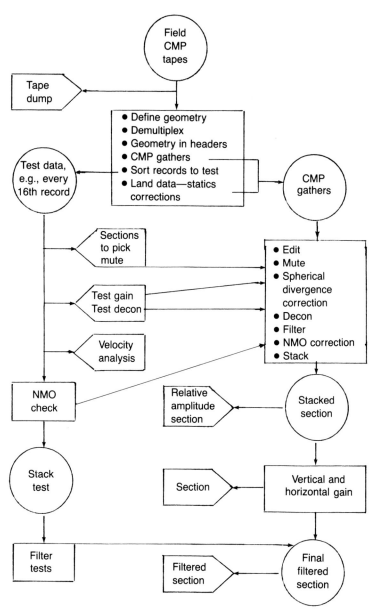

Figure 1-8. Flow chart of the processing steps involved in compositing CMP gathers into a stacked seismic section.

smallest number that a computer works with, namely off or on (0 or 1). According to these definitions there are 96,000 samples in a CMP gather and 288,000,000 samples (4,608,000,000 bits) in a single unstacked seismic line. One weak area in processing technology is in the ability to effectively handle the amounts of data that come from a 3D seismic survey.

Demux is short for *demultiplexing*. When seismic data are collected, they are typically multiplexed. This means that the first sample from all channels being recorded, say 96, is recorded on tape before the second sample from each receiver channel is recorded. This continues with all of second samples being digitized before the third, and so on until all 2000 samples have been digitized. With a 2-ms sample rate, the analog-to-digital converter has to digitize one sample every 20 microseconds (20 × 10^{-6} seconds). These data are not interpretable in a multiplexed format. Geophysicists are interested in evaluating each individual seismic trace as a function of the two-way travel time. In order to get the traces back together, the multiplexing procedure has to be undone. This is a preprocessing step that is normally handled by a minicomputer in large processing shops. Smaller shops have bought minicomputers with extensive seismic processing packages installed on them. It is interesting that these systems often spend 20–40% of their time demultiplexing instead of the seismic processing they were designed for. Ignoring array processor and input/output time, it takes 27 ms of central processor time to demultiplex a trace on a VAX-11/780.[23]

Vibroseis™ correlation was introduced in the acquisition section of this chapter. The basic idea is to spike the reflected Vibroseis™ wavelets so that the data look like they came from an impulsive seismic source. To accomplish this a wavelet that has the same range of frequencies as the Vibroseis™ source wavelet "filters" the demultiplexed field records. This filtering is a mathematical procedure called *cross-correlation*. To get a feel for the procedure, first imagine a raw Vibroseis™ trace. Each reflection consists of a 12-second wavelet instead of a 30-ms spike wavelet. Because there are reflectors every few milliseconds, the trace is the composite of many of these 12-second wavelets overlain on each other. In order to unravel the raw trace, sample 1 on the trace is multiplied with sample 1 on the input sweep, sample 2 with sample 2 on the input sweep, and so on until the 6,000 samples that define the source

Vibroseis℗ wavelet are used. The sum of all of these products becomes the first sample in the correlated output trace. This procedure is then repeated with sample 1 of the source wavelet multiplied with sample 2 of the trace, etc. The sum of these products is sample 2 of the output trace. This multiply-add-shift procedure is repeated for each sample in the recorded trace. When the source wavelet matches the wavelet from a reflected horizon the sum of the products is a large number, or the maximum amplitude on an impulse wavelet from a reflector. When the source wavelet is out of phase with a reflected wavelet, the sum of the products tends to cancel out and the amplitude of that sample is around zero. The result is a seismic trace with impulse-like reflections. This is an example of time series analysis.

CMP gathers are organized using a sorting algorithm. When the seismic source fires and data is recorded by 96 receiver stations along a line, there are also 96 subsurface reflection points. When the source moves forward for the next recording, the subsurface reflection points also move forward by the same distance. If trace 1 from shotpoint 1 is from the same subsurface reflection point as trace 3 from shotpoint 2, these traces are considered to be reflections from the same CMP. To sort the traces that fall at the same CMP location, the first step is to have the source and receiver locations for each shot defined. By definition this specifies the location of each CMP. The sorting procedure is then used to gather all of the traces located at the same CMP location from the field records into CMP gathers.

Decon is short for *deconvolution,* another time series analysis operation. The objective of deconvolution is to undo the effect of an earlier filter action. The earth acts as a filter to seismic waves. One use of deconvolution is to remove the filtering action of a water layer by dereverberating or deringing the data. There are many different types of deconvolution (or dereverberation), and one of the most common examples is predictive deconvolution. The idea here is to use an earlier part of the trace (a waterbottom reflection) to predict and deconvolve a later part of that trace (a multiple). There are regular schools taught by the SEG and other professional groups specifically on deconvolution. (For example, the 1982 SEG distinguished lecturer was Sven Treitel, Amoco research and formerly with the MIT GAG group, and his topic was "Deconvolution: Use But Don't Abuse.") Many geophysicists believe deconvolution has been greatly overused, that the effects on the seismic wavelet are not really understood, and that it is probably better not to do deconvolution. However, there are probably more seismic processors that regularly use decon as a standard processing step.

Muting is a procedure of simply removing noise or other data that affects data quality. This is accomplished by zeroing the amplitude values of those samples on a trace or a record that have strong and recognizable noise waves on them. Figure 1-9 illustrates a raw field record from a 3D survey and what that record looks like after the first arrivals and the air wave were muted.[24] Note that the value of each affected trace is zero in the defined mute window.

Proper *velocity analysis* is critical in order to have confidence in the validity of results that come from seismic data. There are four basic terms for seismic velocity that depend on the model used. Stacking velocity assumes a simple model where there is a constant velocity above a horizontal reflector—an obviously false situation. This velocity is used to maximize events in the compositing or stacking of CMP traces. If the assumption of horizontal layering of the velocity layers is true, then the stacking velocity will approximate RMS (root-mean-square) velocity, a second velocity term. There are specific formulas defining how to determine the RMS velocity, based on knowing the interval velocity of contiguous layers and travel times to reflections. The third term for velocity is average velocity, which is simply the ratio of the depth divided by the seismic travel time to that depth. RMS and average velocity are different ways of averaging interval velocities.[25] Interval velocity refers to the mean velocity measured between different seismic reflections.

The ability to do many seismic processing procedures as well as to convert seismic time information into depth requires that there be a good handle on the seismic velocities.[25] Figure 1-10 is an example of a typical velocity display. The events on the CMP traces have been shifted and correlated to determine which velocities are best to correct for NMO (normal moveout). The RMS velocity is picked from the velocity spectra display that is derived from CMP gathers about every quarter of a mile. This velocity information is often displayed as contours instead of stick-deflections. The power spectrum, between the velocity spectra display and the CMP gather, shows which events correlated best across all of the

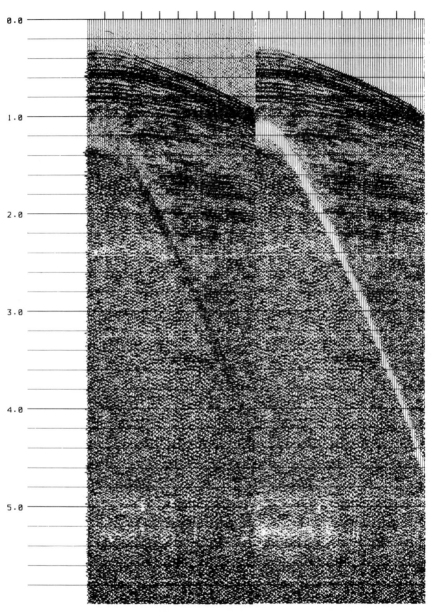

Figure 1-9. The left section is a field record from a 3D seismic survey. The right section is the same record but muted. The first arrivals were zeroed and a window was created through the section that contained the Vibroseis™ generated air wave. (After Huang and Gardner.[24])

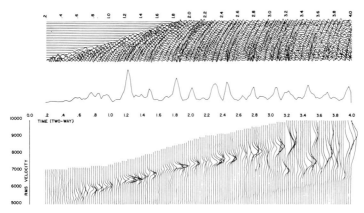

Figure 1-10. This is a velocity spectral display of which the top section is a CMP gather. The single curve in the center is a correlation or power curve defining where in time the events on the CMP are most consistent across the record. The deflections on the velocity spectra show which velocities best flatten events on the CMP gather as a function of time. (After Taner and Koehler.[25])

traces in the CMP gather. Normally, it is not as easy to pick the stacking velocities as in this example. For instance, if the geologic horizons dip, the apparent velocity is quite different from the RMS velocity.

Normal moveout (NMO) is the change in the reflection arrival time because of variations in the source-receiver offsets.[17] NMO is mostly a function of the velocity and offset, but is also affected by the dip of seismic reflectors. The key parameter to determine before NMO can be corrected is the RMS velocity. This velocity is used to line up (flatten) seismic reflection events on each CMP gather before they are stacked. If the NMO correction is done properly, then when these traces are summed, the reflection events from a reflecting horizon will all add together to give a stronger event at that horizon. Because multiples and certain other noise waves do not travel at the correct velocity they are not flattened during NMO correction. This means that when these events are summed, they do not add up as a significant seismic reflector.

Stacking is simply a method to improve the signal-to-noise ratio, by adding reflections together in phase and adding noise out of phase so that it cancels. Two wavelets are in phase if the sample (time) of the maximum amplitude and the zero crossings are the same. The most common type of stacking in a standard seismic processing sequence is to sum the traces in a CMP gather. There are several other types of stacking, all of which are to enhance the seismic reflections and reduce random seismic noise, which increases the signal-to-noise ratio. *Ground mixing* is the combination of several sources or receivers over a limited ground area in the field. *Instrument mixing* is the same thing in the recording truck. Stacking several Vibroseis℠ sweeps is an example of this. Vertical stacking combines traces that have nearly identical source group positions. Uphole stacking averages data from different shot depths after static shifting, based on uphole-time measurements. Common-offset stacking combines data from a limited area for which the source-receiver offset distance is the same. *Velocity filtering* mixes data that have the same apparent dip. *Coherency filtering* combines data which satisfy certain trace-to-trace coherence criteria. Stacking procedures can be based on the sum of seismic trace samples, the weighted average of the sum, the mean value, or other statistical combinations.

Statics are corrections that are applied to seismic data to eliminate the effects of variations in elevation, weathering thickness, or weathering velocity. The weathering layer consists of unconsolidated material near the surface of the earth that rapidly varies in thickness and velocity. The seismic weathering layer is usually different from the geologic weathering layer. The seismic travel time through this layer is normally measured from uphole shot times by a shothole crew or by measuring the first breaks on seismic refraction events that traveled along shallow layers. Underlying the concept of statics corrections is the assumption that a simple time shift of an entire seismic trace will yield the seismic record that would have been recorded if the geophones had been moved downward to a datum plane. This is not strictly true and the effect of vertical and lateral velocity variations also needs to be considered. One of the results of a properly planned 3D seismic survey is a realistic areal map of statics effects. Statics corrections can be made before or after a final stacked section is made. However, it is better to consider this information before stack, because if there is a low-velocity weathering layer delaying the far offset traces and not the near offset traces, then the NMO correction will not accurately align the reflectors. Not doing the statics correction before stack can result in the stacking procedure decreasing the resolution of the seismic image.

Spherical divergence is the decrease in wave strength (energy per unit area of the wavefront) with distance as a result of geometric spreading.[17] Seismic wavefronts continually spread out, and the amount of energy that can be reflected from a horizon decreases as a function of the distance the energy has traveled. The spherical divergence from a point source causes the energy density to decrease inversely as the square of the distance the wave has traveled. The two basic types of signal increase with time (gain) used to correct for spherical divergence during processing are either AGC (automatic gain control) or an exponential gain correction.

AGC algorithms set the maximum gain within a specified time window of a seismic trace to a preset value. As this time window (say, 200 ms) is moved down a trace or seismic section the gain factor is continually being calculated. The result is that the maximum deflections on the seismic trace are approximately the same down the entire section. This same type of procedure is often used in a different processing step to standardize the gain in space or distance along a section. The difference is that the window (several traces wide) used to pick the gain is moved along the section. This is very helpful in being able to do geological structural evaluations of seismic data. However, applying an AGC destroys the relative amplitude information that is critical in evaluating direct hydrocarbon indicators (bright spots) or seismic stratigraphy plays.

An exponential gain correction, on the other hand, keeps the relative amplitude information somewhat more intact by applying a regularly increasing gain curve down the seismic traces and the same gain curve to all of the traces along a section. This means that the samples down the trace are multiplied by a regularly increasing factor instead of a variable amount tied to a moving window. The main purpose for this processing step is to enhance low amplitude reflections that come later in time as an alternate method to correct for the decrease in wave strength with increasing travel-time.

Filtering is a very common seismic processing practice and can happen at any or many stages of the processing sequence. The idea behind filtering is to discriminate against some of the information entering a system. In seismic processing the discriminator is normally frequency (the number of cycles per second of the seismic wavelet) and the system is the seismic trace. Deconvolution is a type of filter operation. As in whitening or optimum filtering the idea is to shape the frequency spectrum according to some knowledge of prior filtering actions, like multiples. The most common seismic processing filters are variations of a *band-pass filter*. A band-pass filter attenuates high and/or low frequencies and only lets those frequencies within a specified range remain on the wavelet. In processing a seismic section it is common to test the effect of different filters on the seismic wavelet. Based on these tests a series of filters that change in time are often applied to some section displays. For instance, the near surface reflections tend to have more high frequency information than the deeper reflections where this energy has been attenuated by the earth filter. Therefore, false high-frequency information should be removed from the deeper part of the section. The inverse of a band-pass filter is a *notch filter*. This is where a specific range of frequencies is removed from the wavelet. The most common example is to remove 60 Hz data, that could have been introduced in the field from power lines, the recording truck, etc. Filtering of seismic data can be misused if the processor does not understand the effect the operation has on the seismic data.

Migration is a mathematical, computer focusing procedure that collapses diffractions and plots reflections from dipping layers in their actual spatial location, instead of at the CMP. Figure 1-11 illustrates the concept of migration. Just as deconvolution was the main seismic topic in the 1960s, migration was emphasized in the 1970s. As a result there are numerous articles, papers and books on the subject of migration. There are four basic mathematical approaches to migration: wave equation; finite-difference; frequency domain approaches; and Kirchhoff migration. Each method has advantages and disadvantages that have been described in the literature.[26] The bottom line is that if the velocity distribution is approximately correct the results from each of these methods is about the same.[27] A synthetic seismic section and the results of a proper migration are illustrated in Figure 1-12.[28] Note that the faults and small anticline have long diffraction tails, and that the basin creates a characteristic bow-tie in the synthetic zero-offset section (Figure 1-12A). These effects are removed with a proper migration (Figure 1-12B). Figure 1-13 illustrates how a frequency

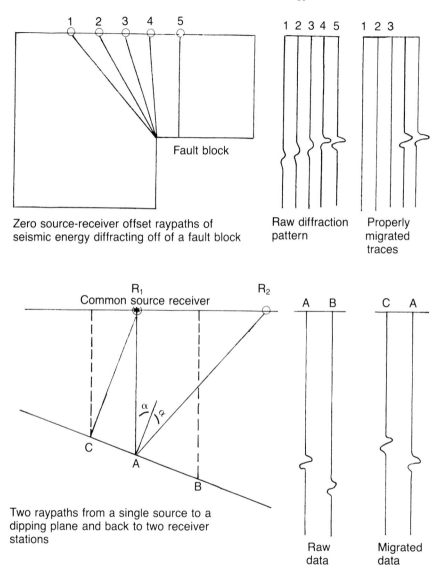

Figure 1-11. Migration is a mathematical, computer focusing procedure that collapses diffractions (top) and plots reflections from dipping layers in their actual spatial location instead of at the CMP (bottom).

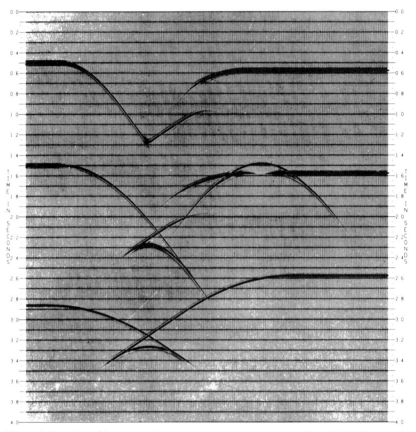

Figure 1-12A. A synthetic seismic section made assuming a zero offset, 8,000 ft/sec, and 50 ft trace spacing. Note the diffractions off of the faults and the small anticline, as well as the "bow-tie effect" in the basins.

domain migration approach can migrate true dips up to 90° using synthetic overthrust model data.[29]

These examples show that very complex 2D or dip direction structures can be properly focused using migration. However, 3D geology requires that a 3D volume of data be migrated in both the dip and strike direction in order to properly focus the data in space and time. The fact that a proper 3D migration of a seismic data volume is a focusing procedure has been vividly illustrated in projection imaging displays of raw and migrated 3D physical model data.[30] The migration procedure does become much more complex in three dimensions, although the complexity is more in

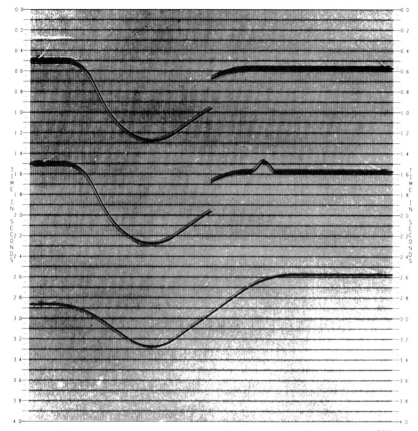

Figure 1-12B. A 2D migrated synthetic wave theory section. (After Schneider.[28])

the required computer processing power than in the algorithms. This increased processing has mostly to do with squaring the number of traces that have to be worked with. The input/output problems associated with working with an aperture of traces around each CMP location also has a major impact on processing needs. There are true 3D migration algorithms that have been implemented. However, it takes on the order of 10^3 more computer power to do a full 3D migration than to migrate a 2D section. One simplification of the 3D migration is to migrate all of the sections along one axis in 2D and then to sort these traces into perpendicular sections and migrate in this direction. This results in reducing

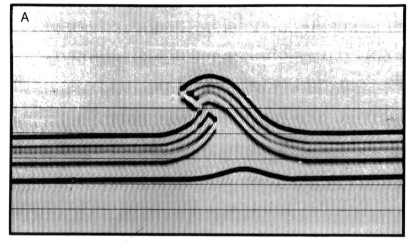

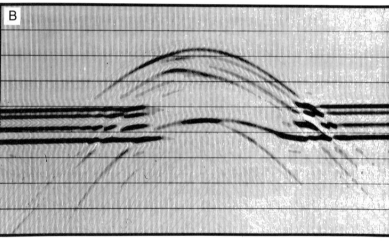

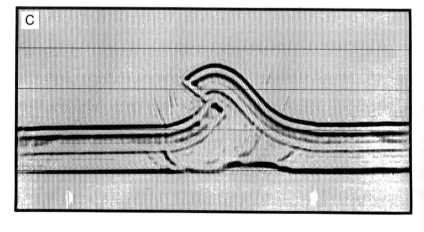

the number of traces to be handled from N^2 to $2N$, where N is the number of traces in the migration aperature.

Figure 1-14 summarizes the processing power required to solve migration problems as they are now defined, as well as projections of future related solutions. The standard 3D migration procedure today would be 2-step (approximate) 3D migration. There is some work being routinely done to do 2D migration before stack and full 3D migration. The computer effort to accomplish these different procedures is measured as a function of what is called a benchmark data unit (BDU) by Johnson and French.[26] One BDU is defined as the computer effort required to resample in time 24 traces of data from 1,500 to 3,000 samples per trace. One BDU on an IBM 3033 central processing unit takes about 0.2 sec.[26] Bill French has timed a BDU on a VAX-11/780 at 1.55 sec for a 20-trace record. This is a composite of CPU and array processor time. These are generalized relationships that actually depend on the hardware and algorithm configuration.

The "unified" solution is a projection of a future processing scheme that attempts to image geologic situations where structure and velocity vary in all directions.[26] This could involve an iterative imaging of structure and velocity step by step from the surface downward. This type of procedure requires a high-speed interactive system in order to optimize migration results by varying the input parameters (velocity, maximum dip angle, frequency range, etc.).[31] Interactive optimization consists of three steps: (1) specify an initial velocity-depth model; (2) migrate the data according to the parameters set in the first step; and (3) compare the migrated results with the input model in order to update the model for the next step. If assumptions are made that by the 1990s three-component recording of a vector wave field will be possible with a 25 meter group spacing, it is possible that the unified approach can be extended to a full elastic migration theory.[26] However, the projected computer time to accomplish this is incomprehensible. Johnson and French have projected the computer times required

---

Figure 1-13. This example of depth migration by time reversal across an overthrust model shows how a frequency domain migration approach can migrate true dips up to 90°. A shows the original overthrust model; B is a synthetic zero/source/receiver section across this model; C shows depth-migrated results. (After Baysal, Sherwood, and Kosloff.[29])

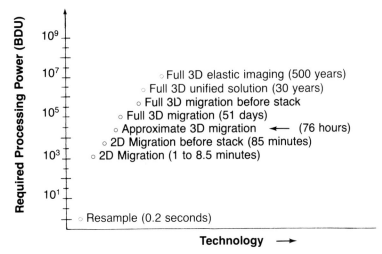

Figure 1-14. Summary of computer processing power estimates in terms of BDU per 24-trace output. A BDU (benchmark data unit) is defined as the computer effort to resample in time 24 traces (1,500–3,000 samples per trace) of data. One BDU on a VAX 11/780 takes 1.6 sec and on an IBM 3033 central processing unit takes 0.2 sec. (After Johnson and French.[26])

to accomplish these various migration options, and they have been summarized in Figure 1-14. The bottom line is that there will continue to be improvements and new developments in seismic processing techniques, if for no other reason than to handle the volumes of data that are being acquired today more efficiently.

INTERPRETATION

Interpretation is quite different from seismic data acquisition and processing. There is experience required to be effective in all three areas. However, standard interpretation techniques are almost more of an art or an apprenticeship learned modus operandi than a science. There are some very straightforward procedures that are followed to do a seismic interpretation. However, these procedures will often vary widely from interpreter to interpreter. One fact that should always hold, and yet too often does not, is that the interpreter should know exactly what has happened to the data prior to it coming to his or her desk. This means that the interpreter should have been involved from the time of the design of the shooting program. This allows him to make sure that the survey grid is properly planned in order to properly cross the geologic structures, provide a fine enough spatial sampling, and tie into previous seismic shooting in the area. Acquisition parameters are often enhanced if the final user (the interpreter) has been involved in establishing them. This should especially be true of setting processing parameters. The new, powerful microcomputers promise to distribute enough computer power to interpreters so that they will be able to optimize key processing steps in order to maximize the information they extract from the seismic section in doing an interpretation.

Understanding the different types of seismic section display is a good place to start a discussion on seismic interpretation. There are three basic types of seismic display. One of the first digital seismic displays was called *variable density (VD)*. A VD section has a point or a small square at each time sample on each trace that is shaded according to the amplitude of the seismic trace. One of the earliest methods of displaying seismic data was as a wiggle trace, like in Figure 1-1. When wiggle traces are superimposed on a variable density section there is additional information available to the interpreter. The most popular display of seismic data is called *wiggle variable area (WVA)*. This type of section has the area between the zero line of the trace and the positive deflections of the trace filled in with black. This results in black events that line up and look like geologic horizons to a seismic interpreter. This type of display can be modified by not displaying the wiggle trace, and just plotting the variable area, and is known as a *variable area section (VA)*. When any of these display formats are presented on a standard seismic section, there is usually considerable vertical exaggeration. Figure 1-15 describes the typical scales worked with in doing seismic interpretation.

A recently published study carried out at Exxon Production Research showed that VD sections are a better display method than the WVA sections under most cases.[32] The industry, in general, does not believe this. This report showed that for sections with a 3.75 in./sec scale and on low contrast photographic paper there is little difference in the VD and WVA sections. However, for displays with small scales or high contrast, the variable density

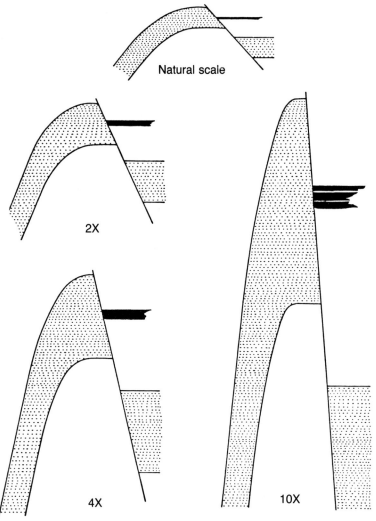

Figure 1-15. Vertical exaggeration allows one to see vertical and horizontal context, but severely distorts bed thickness, structural relationship, fault dip, etc. The vertical exaggeration on a seismic section varies as a function of the velocity of the rocks, but is typically within this range. (After Sheriff.[17])

display is significantly superior. One conclusion was that seismic reflection perceptibility is best for a VD section with time scales in the vicinity of 1.875 in./sec. This is the same type of display that is easiest and best to use in displaying seismic data on a computer graphics terminal either in gray scales or color. However, presently almost all seismic data that an interpreter works with is on large sheets of paper. Also, it is unreasonable to suppose that regional studies and detailed stratigraphic interpretations will use the same display scale.

One of the first things that an interpreter does after getting the assignment to interpret an area is to get the materials together. In practice this should include well log information, gravity maps, magnetic maps, geological information, etc. For the purposes of this chapter, we will assume that the only thing that the interpreter needs to get are the seismic sections over the area he or she is to work. It will also be assumed that the library is well organized and serves the user by providing original copies of the sections for reproduction in a reasonable time frame, and that the reproduction department can provide copies of the sections rapidly. Unmigrated and 3D migrated sections must have all of the crossing seismic line tie points marked so that the sections can be folded and tied to crossing lines to evaluate orthogonal common events. Sections that have been migrated in 2D will not tie at the line crossings. In practice the clerical work of getting the sections together, marking the tie lines, and generally organizing the data is a significant time factor in an interpretation project. This is an area that can be greatly improved by establishing an effective data base management system as described in Chapter 10.

Once the data are together, an interpreter will often take a couple of days to just look at the data and get a feel for the major structural trends, locate the most significant anomalous events, and tie together other geological information. Seismic sections are hung on the wall or otherwise prominently displayed. At this time, some of the major faults and trends might be noted on the seismic sections or on a small-scale location map. This overview is normally best accomplished using dip lines, because they tend to be easier to interpret. In areas that have complex faulting, like a growth fault provinance, it is often useful to map the location of the faults at different travel times. This is known as a fault plane map, and provides the interpreter with a feel for the geologic structural trends that will effect the interpretation.

Normally, the horizons that are going to be mapped will be based on previous interpretations, a co-worker's notes about the area, or well log information, like a sonic log. Once the events are identified and marked at, say, a well location on the seismic section, the next step is to follow these geologic horizons along the seismic section. Usually, these events are marked with colored pencils. As a horizon comes to a crossing line, the crossing line is folded at the tie point (the same CMP on two crossing seismic lines). This same procedure is followed until seismic picks (colored horizons) are made around a loop back to the starting location. By tying a horizon together on four mutually perpendicular seismic sections that form a loop, the interpreter has reasonable confidence that he is picking the same geologic horizon on each of the sections.

In areas where there is complex faulting, it is critical that the interpreter be able to tie the loops in order to minimize the possibility of jumping the interpretation mark to a different layer on the other side of a fault. The paper sections are folded so that the fault is hidden and events directly correlated to help to determine how much throw there is on fault. Often, there are "misties" in taking seismic picks around a loop. (A mistie is where the seismic event is followed around a loop, but when the picks get back to the original section they are on a different reflector than they started out on.) These misties can be due to subtle faults or stratigraphic effects that change the wavelet shape in a manner that is hard to interpret. However, it is more common, particularly with older surveys, that there were problems with the location of the seismic line. This is particularly a problem for offshore surveys that were shot before there was enough satellite coverage to obtain sufficiently accurate navigation information and the related source-receiver location information.

A common mistie difficulty is caused by reversal of polarity between crossing sections. Particularly for older data the polarity may not be known or possibly even incorrectly stated.[33] Filtering, deconvolution, and other processing parameters can add shifts in the data that make it hard to determine the polarity. Mispicking or differences in the stacking velocities can also result in misties of different sections. Often this is solved by doing most of the interpretation on a regular grid of data that was acquired as a set of data and processed with similar parameters. Previously shot sections are worked into the interpretation to solve specific problems, like misties, where there is insufficient coverage.

A related problem is choosing events that are artifacts of the seismic reflection method. Multiple reflections within a layer are an example of the false seismic events that can be interpreted as a reflected event off of a geologic horizon. Figure 1-16 is a marine seismic section from the Gulf of Alaska[34] that illustrates the problems that multiples can cause. In this case the multiple is fairly straightforward to see. It consists of energy that traveled from the source to the sea bottom and back to the ocean surface, was bounced again and went back down to the sea bottom and back to the receiver. This multiple bouncing can be repeated many times as is seen on this section. Particularly notice the left-hand side of the section, because there are at least two strong multiples that can be easily seen. They are recognizable because the event on each trace is two or three times as deep as the water bottom (i.e., a multiple of the two-way travel time through the ocean). There are numerous other examples of the type of insights that an interpreter gains with experience. The bottom line is to come up with an interpretation that is geologically sound and can be tested by the drillbit.

The primary objective of interpretation is to map the geologic horizons, that is, to determine the geological structure. A second objective is to determine the nature of the rocks and the third to determine the nature of the fluids in the pore spaces of the rocks.[35] The second and third categories fall under the heading of seismic stratigraphy, and are covered in more detail elsewhere in the literature.[5,6]

Figure 1-17 is an example of a one-line seismic interpretation. In this case, the structure being evaluated is an overthrust in the Green River Basin.[35] The faulting and horizon picks look obvious after they are marked on the section. However, it is not always so easy to come up with a geologic explanation for data on the seismic section. Picking seismic events is the key interpretation step. There are numerous other steps that must be followed to complete the interpretation, but many, if not portions of all of them, can be automated with the proper hardware and software.

After the horizons are interpreted and tied together around loops on the seismic sections, the data are ready to be set up for

(text continued on page 54)

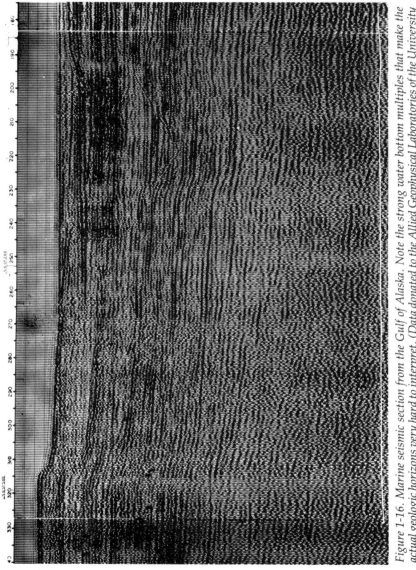

Figure 1-16. Marine seismic section from the Gulf of Alaska. Note the strong water bottom multiples that make the actual geologic horizons very hard to interpret. (Data donated to the Allied Geophysical Laboratories of the University of Houston by Karl Thompson and Associates.)

Figure 1-17. An interpreted seismic section across the Wind River Over-thrust. (After Steiner.[36])

contouring. A standard way of accomplishing this is to set up some computer coding sheets for a geophysical technician to use. The travel time is recorded for each end point and inflection point of the seismic horizon. There are several digitizing systems that allow an interpreted seismic section to be directly digitized on a large digitizing tablet. Often, in practice, the horizon travel times are hand posted on a location map. There is much less chance of error if the horizons are digitized as they are interpreted. However, this is not what is usually done. For those times that are digitized from an interpreted section or key punched from computer data sheets, there are mapping systems that allow this digital data to be directly put out via a pen plotter or electrostatic plotter onto a large scale map. All of this work is to transfer the horizon travel-times onto a workmap so that a contoured map can be produced.

Figure 1-18 is an example of the final result of seismic acquisition, processing and interpretation—a contour map.[36] Tradition-

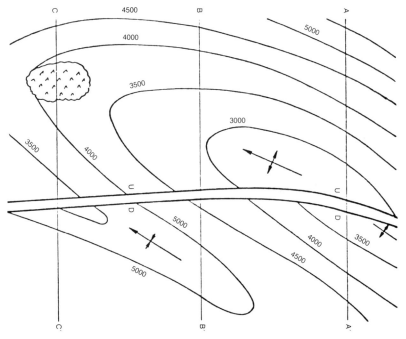

Figure 1-18. Contour map showing a fault, a salt piercement, and a basin. (After Sheriff.[17])

ally, the contour map has been used for decisions where to drill, for management or partnership presentations, and for compact storage. This particular contour map is idealized for training purposes, but it does show the major high, a large fault, a downthrown basin with a structural high, and a salt piercement. It is an interesting fact that each interpreter has his or her own style of contouring. His or her style is almost as distinctive as handwriting. Most interpreters prefer to do their final maps by hand, rather than use a computer contouring package.

One area where the computer contouring packages are used more is in making isochron maps. Isochron means equal time, and an isochron map is the difference between two time maps. There are also isopach (equal depth) and isolith (equal lithology) maps that can be made. If a set of maps has been created for different layers and the contour information is digital, then the computer can be used to generate a first cut at making the isochron maps. Because of the unique interpretation background and style that an experienced interpreter has, hand-contoured maps will probably never be completely replaced. There are many variations of converting a time map into a isochron map that do make computer maping technology more attractive. These include tying a velocity function(s) to the time maps to generate a depth map, etc. Computers are and can be used more by interpreters to do a map migration of a time or depth structure map, calculate potential reservoir volumes, etc.

One interpretation technique that is really changing the quality of seismic exploration interpretation is the use of time-slice or horizontal seismic sections. Starting with 3D seismic survey, a sequence of time slices or seismic sections at a constant travel-time are converted to 16 mm film. G. S. I. has developed a special interpretation table that projects the time-slice section onto the work area of a rear projection drafting table. Because the seismic sections are in movie format, they can be moved through forward and backward, fast or slow, or stopped. The movement of data allows an interpreter to visually determine if the structure is an anticline or a syncline, where the faults run in space, etc.

A contour map can be easily generated with this system. A piece of clear paper is mounted on the work area and a horizontal section displayed. The interpreter then simply traces the outline of an event of interest. Then, the movie is moved forward a few frames (depending on the contour interval), the map paper left in place and the contouring procedure repeated. Building a contoured interpretation based on the data volume is an important development in interpretation technology. This technique, when tied to standard vertical interpretation techniques, promises to open a lot of new doors for improving seismic interpretation techniques. By the end of 1983, there should be at least three working systems available to accomplish this same type of interpretation task on an interactive computer graphics terminal.

Once the maps are generated, an interpreter is responsible for finalizing the results in a report and then selling his concepts to management. A typical report will include: an introduction; a description of the data used specifing information like statics adjustments to tie different surveys; a summary of the geology and the structural framework; the relationship between wells and seismic data; an explanation of the reflectors that were picked; a detailed description of the interpretation of each horizon mapped; a summary of the main prospective structures; a recommendation for future work; guidance on future development policy; and a summary of the work undertaken.[33] If these reports are put together right, it is of great benefit to later interpreters that work an adjacent area or just want some practical examples. The presentation of materials to management and partners requires professionalism. One of the things that keeps interpreters from achieving their full potential is not being able to "sell" the product to the decision makers.

In looking to the next few years of seismic interpretation, there are several needs that are expected to be met much better because of new technology. A key development will be the building of workstations for interactive interpretation. With the power that is being put in small microprocessors, it seems reasonable to project that interpreters will be able to do many things online that have traditionally been overnight batch jobs. For example, if there was some reprocessing that needed to be done to evaluate a specific anomaly, this data could be submitted locally by the user from an interactive workstation. Synthetic modeling algorithms and trace attribute analysis should be possible to do within a small workstation. If the workstation is tied to a larger data base management system, then data can be interactively retrieved, magnified, polarity switched, scaled, and color assignment given on a high-resolution color graphics terminal. The same horizon selection that is done with a colored pencil can be done at an interpretation workstation interactively with a cursor or automatically by trace to trace correlation. In fact, as better application software packages are developed and released, it is reasonable to expect to see more computer power at the fingertips of an interpreter. This allows an interpreter to think of interactively flattening a horizon, filling contour maps with solid colors, specifying data color assignments, and doing other things that require a fair amount of local processing power. These types of operations require interaction with the data and cannot be used in a batch environment.

SUMMARY

Exploration geophysics is based on the science of reflection seismology. The concepts behind exploring for hydrocarbons, using techniques based on the reflection of seismic waves off of geologic layering in the sedimentary section, are relatively simple. In fact, some of the assumptions used are too simplified and they need to be expanded in order to really describe what is happening to seismic waves in the subsurface. Although the science is new and has only existed in the twentieth century, there has been considerable growth. Economics has been a major factor in this growth, but probably more important has been the creativity of the people that have been attracted to exploration seismology. Since the first work with reflection seismology in the early 1920s, doodlebuggers have been trying to build a better "mousetrap" or improve the method of seeing in the earth's subsurface with seismic energy. This has resulted in a major impact on science and society as a whole. The work of the GAG group at MIT in the mid-1950s had a major impact on the computer revolution. Array processors were developed in the late 1960s, largely as a response to seismic processing needs. The vector processors of the late 1970s were developed with a similar need in mind, specifically to sell computer equipment to oil companies. On the more pragmatic side, the success of oil exploration techniques has helped provide the energy necessary to build society as it is today. The implementation of new technologies in seismic acquisition, processing, and interpretation has been a key to the success of the reflection seismic method. As hydrocarbon reserves decrease and the deposits left to find become smaller and are in more complex geological environments, it will be more important than ever for explorationists to exploit new developments that improve the probability of successful well completions.

REFERENCES

1. McDonald, J. M., Gardner, G. H. F., and Morris, R. I., "Reservoir Characterization by Areal Seismic Methods," Proceedings of International Meeting on Petroleum Engineering, Beijing, China, March 1982, Soc. of Pet. Eng., V. 2, pp. 43–55.
2. Nettleton, L. L., *Geophysical Prospecting for Oil*, McGraw-Hill Book Company, Inc., pp. 280–281, 1940.
3. Woods, J. P., "A Seismic Model Using Sound Waves in Air," *Geophysics*, V. 40, No. 4, pp. 593–607, 1975.
4. Widess, M. B., "How Thin Is a Thin Bed?," *Geophysics*, V. 38, No. 6, pp. 1176–1180, 1973.
5. Payton, C. E., *Seismic Stratigraphy—Applications to Hydrocarbon Exploration*, AAPG Memoir 26, Tulsa, OK, 516 pp., 1977.
6. Sheriff, R. E., *Seismic Stratigraphy*, IHRDC, Boston, MA, 227 pp., 1980.
7. Nelson, H. R., Jr., "Modeling Resolves Complex Seismic Events," *World Oil*, pp. 61–70, Feb. 1, 1982.
8. Kosloff, D. D. and Reshef, M., "Elastic Forward Modeling," SAL Annual Progress Review, V. 10, pp. 115–185, 1982.
9. McCormack, M. D., Dunbar, J. A. and Sharp, W. W., "A Case Study of Stratigraphic Interpretation Using Shear and Compressional Seismic Data," Paper S2.5 SEG Convention, Dallas, TX, 1982 (see also Technical Program Abstracts and Biographies, pp. 21–22, 1982).
10. Dix, C. H., *Seismic Prospecting for Oil*, Harper and Brothers Press, New York, p. 4, 1952.
11. Sheriff, R. E. and Geldart, L. P., *Exploration Seismology*, Cambridge University Press, Cambridge, England, 2 Vol., 1982.
12. Sheriff, R. E., "Eclectic History of Seismic Exploration," paper S7.1, SEG Convention, Houston, TX, 1981 (see also abstract, *Geophysics*, V. 47, No. 4, p. 468, 1982).
13. Pankonien, L. J., "What's Happening in the United States?," *World Oil*, pp. 25–27, Aug. 1, 1982.
14. Sheriff, R. E., University of Houston, personnel communication, Houston, TX, 1982.
15. Schneider, W. A., *et al*, "Land Seismic Source Study," Paper S5.8 SEG Convention, Dallas, TX, 1982 (see also Technical Program Abstracts and Biographies, pp. 71–72, 1982).

16. Poulter, T. C., "The Poulter Seismic Method of Geophysical Exploration," *Geophysics*, V. 15, No. 2, pp. 181–207, 1950.
17. Sheriff, R. E., *Encyclopedic Dictionary of Exploration Geophysics*, SEG, Tulsa, OK, 266 pp., 1973.
18. Prince, E. R., III, Digicon Geophysical, personal communication, East Grinstead, England, 1982.
19. Klaassen, K. B. and van Peppen, J. C. L., "A Novel High-Resolution Geophone," 44th meeting of EAEG, Cannes, France, June 8–11, 1982 (see also Technical Program and Abstracts of Papers, pp. 5–6).
20. Gal'perin, E. I., *Vertical Seismic Profiling*, SEG, Tulsa, OK, 270 pp., 1974.
21. Senti, R. J., *et al*, "Special Report Geophysical Activity in 1981, Table 17 Worldwide Geophysical Activity," *The Leading Edge*, V. 1, No. 4, p. 50, 1982.
22. Flin, E. A., Robinson, E. A. and Treitel, S., "The MIT Geophysical Analysis Group Reports," *Geophysics*, V. 32, No. 3, pp. 411–525, 1967.
23. Chou, L., "The Use of State-of-the-Art Computing Systems in a Research Environment," SAL Semi-annual Progress Review, V. 9, pp. 231–250, 1982.
24. Huang, H. C. and Gardner, G. H. F., "Preliminary Three-Dimensional Data Processing Programs for Seismic Data," SAL Annual Progress Review, V. 10, pp. 289–290, 1982.
25. Taner, M. T. and Koehler, F., "Velocity Spectra-Digital Computer Derivation and Applications of Velocity Functions," *Geophysics*, V. 34, No. 6, pp. 859–881, 1969.
26. Johnson, J. D. and French, W. S., "Migration—The Inverse Method," in *Concepts and Techniques in Oil and Gas Exploration*, edited by K. C. Jain and R. J. P. de Figueiredo, SEG, Tulsa, OK, pp. 115–157, 1982.
27. Gardner, G. H. F., University of Houston, personnel communication, Houston, TX, 1982.
28. Schneider, W. A., "Integral Formulation for Migration in Two and Three Dimensions," *Geophysics*, V. 43, No. 1, pp. 49–76, 1978.
29. Baysal, E., Sherwood, J. W. C. and Kosloff, D. D., "Depth Migration by Time Reversal," SAL Annual Progress Review, V. 10, pp. 305–324, 1982.
30. Harris, L. D. and Nelson, H. R., Jr., "Three-Dimensional Display and Analysis of Seismic Volume Images," SEG Proceedings, V. 2, pp. 2037–2045, 1981.
31. Berkhout, A. J. and Larson, D., High-Speed Interactive System for Interpretive Migration," Paper S1.5 SEG Convention, Dallas, TX, 1982 (see also Technical Program Abstracts and Biographies, pp. 7–8, 1982).
32. Feagin, F. J., "Seismic Data Display and Reflection Perceptibility," *Geophysics*, V. 46, No. 2, pp. 106–120, 1981.
33. McQuillin, R., Bacon, M., Barclay, W., *An Introduction to Seismic Interpretation*, Gulf Publishing Company, Houston, TX, pp. 70–80, 1979.
34. Marine Gulf of Alaska Data Donated to the AGL of the University of Houston, Karl Thompson and Associates, Houston, TX, 1981.
35. Steiner, C. T., AGL at the University of Houston Unpublished Report, Wind River Overthrust Data Provided by Elf Aquitaine, Houston, TX, 1981.
36. Sheriff, R. E., *A First Course in Geophysical Exploration and Interpretation*, International Human Resources Development Corporation, Boston, MA, pp. 206–217, 1978.

CHAPTER 2

Technological Trends

This chapter is a generalized overview of the new technologies that are being used today in exploration geophysics. New data collection methods, processing developments, interactive interpretation techniques and the hands-on training of tomorrow's explorationists are summarized. Trends and developments that point to new tools and new exploration methods are included. The remainder of the book will expand on particular technologies in respect to their expected effects on geophysical exploration methods in the 1980s.

The increased rate of technological breakthroughs during the last decade points to the 1980s as the time for solving many of the problems traditionally faced by explorationists. Today's geophysicist is looking for smaller and more complex fields. The most modern techniques and tools are required to find small plays that are structurally or stratigraphically separated from previous discoveries already in production. The recent well-publicized wildcatting successes in the Utah and Wyoming overthrust belt, as well as in other complex areas, underline the value of employing the most modern exploration methods available. Since 1973, oil and gas economics have pointed to an ever increasing use of the new and expensive exploration tools at the forefront of technology.

DATA COLLECTION TECHNIQUES

Micro-Computers

Imagine a scenario where an observer on a seismic crew gets an Apple computer for a Christmas present. After all, he or she works with computers and would enjoy playing with such a toy. Alternatively, it might just as well have been a Radio Shack TRS-80, a Grid, an IBM personal computer, a Compaq or one of a dozen other brands of micro-computers. In following the logical consequence of this fictional situation, the bottom line is that this "toy" soon becomes a very useful tool for several members of the crew. An impact printer is obtained and the observer is soon using the computer to keep track of maintenance schedules, crew breaks and vacations, and the daily log of data collection.

The permit agent finds the "toy" to be a tremendous aid as a portable word processor. He uses the computer to type out multiple agreements where the only change is the name of a landowner. The surveyor discovers the ease of using the machine to check, type out, and store survey notes. The observer develops an accounting package for the party manager to reduce the handling expenses of $150,000 per month.

A quality control geophysicist visits the crew for a week and becomes enamored with the "toy." The first day he creates noise response curves. This is followed by his outlining a method for designing the layout of optimal field acquisition programs within the limitations of topography, permits, and culture. The computer is introduced to other company seismic crews, and within two years there is a micro-computer users group sharing ideas and successes. Fictional? Observe what is happening with seismic crews and this will not seem far out for very much longer, if in fact it is now.

Surveying Improvements

One of the most critical problems in seismic data collection is accurate spatial location. Surveying and navigation errors are still the major problem in accurately tying different seismic surveys together. Accurate interpretation and proper processing are possible only if the data location is accurately recorded. There have been many advances in the last few years, and there is research in several other areas that herald new technologies to meet the needs of accurate surveying.

Satellite location is becoming commonplace on marine crews. With more satellite passes it is becoming easier to get a quicker and much more accurate location. The portable Magnavox satellite positioning station can determine position accurately within 3 meters latitude and longitude and 10 meters elevation from 40 satellite passes at Wyoming latitudes, in less than 4 days. By translocation from a known position within 200 miles, the horizontal accuracy is ±1 meter and the vertical accuracy is ±3 meters.[1]

Leo Romeyn of Geodetic Surveys pointed out to the author that by using satellite point positioning techniques and applying rotation and scale, a 2 meter vertical accuracy can be obtained under the same conditions. With a previously surveyed geoidal profile and using the translocation short-arc techniques, positions with ±40 cm (x,y,z) can be obtained. However, there are new problems created by this extraordinary accuracy. For example, it may be found that county lines, property boundaries, and even well locations are not actually located where the legal descriptions indicate.

The new electronic measuring devices are providing significantly more accurate land surveying records. These devices are accurate to within 1 cm over 1.6 km. The slope is off less than 30 cm per 1.6 km, and a careful surveyor will only be off 60 cm over 40 km. This can be improved by taking accurate temperature and pressure measurements since they affect light transmission. The controls are as easy to use as a hand-held calculator. The LED (light emitting diode) displays are easy to read and not subject to variations between surveyors, as can occur with a transit.

There are, of course, limitations. The equipment can not be used on extremely hot days when there are strong heat waves or when there is must dust in the air. It is hard to use a laser diode device in heavy brush, where part of the light to and from the reflector is scattered. However, it is a tremendous advantage to be able to record the survey notes in the field on a digital memory device. This minimizes the standard surveying mistakes that come from poorly written notes, copying notes, keypunch errors, etc. Digitized shotpoint location numbers can be automatically dumped onto a cassette or put into the data tape header by using the doghouse (recording truck) computer. In the evening the surveyor not only saves the time he used to spend working up his notes, but he can use available software/hardware combinations to automatically dump the notes out onto a shotpoint location map.

A dream of geophysicists concerned with the problem of accurate spatial location is to have a self-locating geophone. There are "chains" available that are filled with fluid. When used to chain between shotpoint locations along a line, the elevation differential between different shotpoints is recorded. Devices that triangulate on individual geophones in a two-dimensional receiver pattern also are being developed.

Source/Receiver Improvements

Compressional-wave vibrators have become a standard method of data collection. A vibrator crew can, under most conditions, get more production than a crew tied to shot hole drillers. The environmental improvement is evident in the field. Vibrators have been made larger, modified to be more versatile, and improved for more reliability. One new technique is to vary the frequency on the different vibrator move-ups at the same shot point to increase the signal-to-noise ratio. Some recording systems allow the correlation of each different source wavelet (as related to the input frequency range at each move-up) with the reflected energy as the data is recorded. This type of "real-time" correlator box greatly reduces the amount of data that is stored on magnetic tape.

Shear wave vibrators, introduced in the late 1970s, have four "pyramids" on the base of the vibrator pad that are worked down into the ground to get a coupling. The plate, vibrated from side to side instead of up and down, creates shear wave energy rather than standard P-waves or compressional energy. Although this technology has not yet proved as fruitful as was hoped, it illustrates the innovative attempts being made by geophysicists to find what is in the subsurface.

There are new sources that are being tested, ranging from a marine steam gun that does not produce a bubble to a portable land source that fires a small shotgun shell for shallow work. In areas only accessible by foot, crews use backpacks or helicopters to bring in portable drills for planting shallow dynamite seismic sources. Surface and staked explosives also are being used more widely. Marine Vibroseis™ is being planned for use in environmentally fragile areas, such as the Florida Everglades.[2]

Not only must new energy be developed, but traditional ones must be better understood. This is why work like Bill Schneider's "Source Signature Study," sponsored by the Colorado School of Mines and an industrial consortium, is so important. Understanding the seismic sources will allow explorationists to determine the best ways to increase accessibility to remote areas and still minimize environmental damage.

There are also new developments with the phones that receive the seismic energy. The development of shear wave equipment has resulted in the need for a string of geophones that record energy along one axis. The next step beyond shear wave phones will be the development and use of three-component geophones for reflection seismology. Three-component geophones are presently being used for downhole recording, or vertical seismic profiling. Another improvement for land receivers will be self-locating geophones. Marine hydrophone cables are closer to accomplishing this, with "birds" that are used to control the depth and drift of the cable.

Advances in Recording Technology

Rapid developments in the electronics and communications industries have been mirrored by developments in geophysical recording equipment. New recording devices have more channels and record more samples per second. Multi-channel crews currently in the field record up to 1,024 channels at one time. It is anticipated that this will expand to 4,096 channels within the next few years. Presently, the crews with this many channels record only a sign-bit, i.e., 0 or 1, for each recorded sample. A standard seismic trace is built from this data by correlation. Recording 16-bits of data per sample is the present standard.

There are several types of multi-channel crews that record 16-bit data in 4-channel remote memory boxes. One portable recording device stores this data on cassette tapes. Another system uses wire line telemetry to send the data to the recording truck. Still a different recording system returns the data to the doghouse by means of radio telemetry. With the improvements in satellite communications it does not take much imagination to see the day coming when data will be radioed directly to a central processing center from the field.

The development of faster, smaller, and less expensive memory not only affects the number of channels recorded, but also the sampling rate. It is not uncommon to do high-resolution surveys with a 1 millisecond sampling rate or less. Data is traditionally recorded at 4 milliseconds per sample.

The development of computer bubble memory devices is an example of a new technology that is expected to change seismic recording boxes. These changes will be expanded with parallel developments in other areas. For example, the research being done in fiber optics data transmission will affect seismic recording instruments. Developing ways to record with variable precision from 1 bit to 16 bits will affect the amount of data to be recorded on new high density recording medium, like 6,250 bpi (bits per inch) tapes and eventually video or optical discs.

The potential use of these recording technology changes is being hinted at by the use of mini-computers in the field for doing the processing to prepare for migration. There are several marine data collection systems that have full processing capability aboard the seismic ship. One company accomplishes field premigration processing with land crews using mini-computers installed in large trucks.

3D Seismic Techniques

Seismic reflection studies are undertaken for the purpose of solving geological problems that are invariably 3D (three-dimensional). The earth is 3D, and yet traditional seismic reflection techniques are tied to collection of 2D seismic sections. Three-dimensional seismic techniques include collecting seismic traces over an area, processing these traces, and interpreting the subsurface geology from this data. The simplest component method of collecting seismic over an area is to place the receivers along one line and shoot into these receivers along a perpendicular line. The resulting midpoints cover a two-dimensional area, and the seismic traces represent a 3D volume of the earth. The extension from profile lines to areal coverage brings seismic data into conformance with the geological, geochemical and potential data available over the same area.[3]

By properly planning a 3D survey, seismic crews can collect enough data to accurately evaluate a geological problem cost-effectively. Table 2-1 shows a comparison of the data collection statistics for two experimental surveys using the same crew and the same system.[4] Note that twice as many traces are collected in

Table 2-1
Areal vs. Linear Survey Data

	AREAL	LINEAR
Type	Crossed Arrays	CDP
Channels	96	96
Length	∞	22 miles
Area	2 miles × 4 miles	0
Grid	50 feet	50 feet
Redundancy	4	8
Number of Traces	80,000	40,000
Volume	16 sq. mi.	0
Time	9 days	29 days
Source	Dynamite	Dynamite

one-third of the time with the same crew when using areal survey techniques, and that this data more readily lends itself to the understanding of a 3D geologic setting as it exists in nature. Further, the volume of information produced in collecting areal survey is a basic key to the merging of reflection seismology with reservoir evaluation and with other production techniques.

PROCESSING TECHNOLOGY

Over the last decade processing techniques have developed even faster than the changes in field techniques previously described. A majority of the topics described in the literature fall into the four main topics of wave-equation migration, seismic inversion, wavelet processing and deconvolution, and statics and velocity estimation.[5] Transition from conventional 2D to 3D processing techniques is becoming more common.

Processing technology improvements will for the most part be an extension of present capabilities. There will be more near surface, high resolution analysis to correct for weathering effects. Methods for doing statics corrections for 3D data are being developed. Procedures for doing 3D velocity analysis where lines cross and dealing with 3D volumes of data are being polished and put into production. Migration is being expanded to 3D with the standard Kirchoff, F-K, and finite difference methods. New methods of seismic stripping, depth migrating and direct inversion are being perfected. Forward modeling, or the inverse procedure of migration, is developing in a parallel manner. It is even possible that an exact solution of the wave equation will be developed.

One key question is whether it is possible to make computers that can efficiently handle the volumes of data that are being collected. Input and output of the data volumes will become a key concern to those trying to process these data volumes.

Distributed Processing

Geophysical processing in the 1980s appears to be headed towards heavy use of small computers. The VAX 11/780 and Perkin-Elmer mini-computers are being enhanced and marketed by several of the seismic contracting companies. Having multi-processing capabilities, these computers manage the scheduling of processing jobs automatically, and multi-programming capabilities allow many users to be working with the system at what appears to be the same time. Other mini-computers are made by Data General, Raytheon, SEL, etc. These computers have seismic processing software packages and can be configured with array processors, mass storage devices, rasterizers, 22-inch 200 dot-per-inch electrostatic plotters, 1,000 dot-per-inch laser film plotters, high-resolution display devices, programming terminals, etc. It is also possible to front end these computers to a large mainframe computer that will handle extensive number crunching.

The development of very powerful micro-computers promises to further "distribute" some processing procedures to the office of a seismic processor or interpreter. There are multibus micro-computer systems bases on the Motorola 68000 and Intel 8086/87 chips that promise to open a new world to individual explorationists. Apollo Computers and Landmark Graphics Corporations are two examples of this type of system. These systems will be window's through which explorationists can access very large computer networks.

Super Computers

The new vector computers can run at least 1,000 times faster than the largest scalar computer available, if the software is properly vectorized for parallel processing. The major vector computer systems are the Cray-1 or X-MP and the CDC-203 or 205. A simplified description of how these phenomenal computation speeds are achieved can be shown by a couple of comparisons.

First, instead of processing repetitive mathematical or logical operations by going through each program step "n" times, a vector computer will process the repetitive steps in parallel. Second, the data is run through processing pipes that change it on the fly (as quickly as it can be cycled through the pipe). This is similar to how an array processor works (see Chapter 5). Assuming some basic input/output problems can be solved, it is estimated that a 2D fourier synthetic modeling program that takes 10 hours to run on a VAX will take 5 minutes on a CDC-205.[6] The movement of the data is very critical with the improved processing speeds, and this is why these vector computers will have several of the largest scalar processors simultaneously feeding them data.

With the tremendous amount of data involved in a 3D survey there is a real need for geophysicists to take advantage of these new computer capabilities. There is considerable improvement needed on the methods of moving the data to where it can be used, so the computer is not input/output bound. As inversion and forward modeling techniques are improved, it is feasible to see iterative seismic section matching techniques developed. This is similar in scope and complexity to work being done in the area of reservoir analysis.

INTERACTIVE INTERPRETATION

Improved methods of manipulating and viewing the large volumes of data available to today's explorationist are desperately needed. Determining subsurface geology in order to find hydrocarbon traps is the name of the game. Industry preparations for developing computer data bases have been described in the literature.[7]

Dovetailing nicely with computer improvements and data storage/retrieval systems are the improvements in display technologies. There are some procedures that are being done interactively. The ability to interactively display and interpret 3D volumes of data is getting closer to reality. In the mean time, many geophysicists, especially independent consultants, are developing interpretation aids on their home micro-computers. This work includes synthetic trace programs, map migration routines, etc.

New Display Equipment

There have been tremendous advances in developing new inexpensive raster and storage tube terminals. The resolution is increasing from less than 512 by 512 pixels (single picture elements) for home television to multiple memory planes of 1,024 by 1,024 pixel resolution. CRT (cathode ray tube) display of satellite imagery data is the most common example of this picture resolution. The resolution allows enough data to be displayed to allow interactive interpretation (Figure 2-1). In order to get an overview of a geologic objective, the rapid display of a sequence of 2D digital images can be used. For normal seismic section interpretation, this can aid the continuity of following a fault or other anomaly. The effectiveness of moving through a series of horizontal seismic sections has been shown by G.S.I.'s Seiscrop™ presentations.[8]

When the geophysical interpreter steps into the world of 3D data volumes, there needs to be a way to display the data in 3D space. One tool that creates an apparent 3D display is high-resolution vector refresh graphics.[9] These display devices have been used for some time in the computer-aided design of 3D objects. One such display creates a full-color, 3D set of vectors that can be rotated (Figure 2-2). Another has a raster segment generator that displays up to 240 traces with 1,000 samples on each trace simultaneously (Figure 2-3). Vectors with 3D coordinates are drawn as an interpretation over these sections. As the sections are moved through the data volume the interpretation becomes a series of rotatable 3D vectors.

There are several true 3D display devices that have the potential of helping in the evaluation of 3D data volumes. One uses a high resolution electrostatic scope to create a series of virtual images in 3D space behind a vibrating mirror.[10,11] Another device, developed at M.I.T., uses computer controlled LED's on a rotating plane to create a 3D image.[12] A third method uses multiple CRT's and beam splitters to place the images in 3D space.[13] The simplest 3D illusion is made by facing two parabolic mirrors together, so that an object

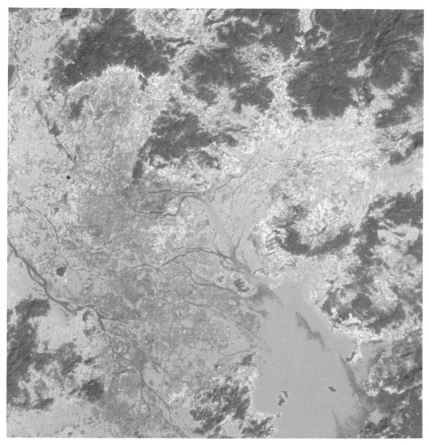

Figure 2-1. Example of an enhanced Landsat, satellite imagery, photograph that is currently used as a primary exploration tool. Efforts are underway to increase the resolution of display equipment so that it approaches the resolution attained by such Landsat images.

placed inside on the base mirror is optically projected above a hole in the base of the top mirror.[14] However, there will be several years of research work before any of these devices will meet the needs of geophysical interpreters.

Interactive Interpretation Consoles

There are several companies that have developed mapping consoles. These normally use a storage tube display and are tied to a

(text continued on page 74)

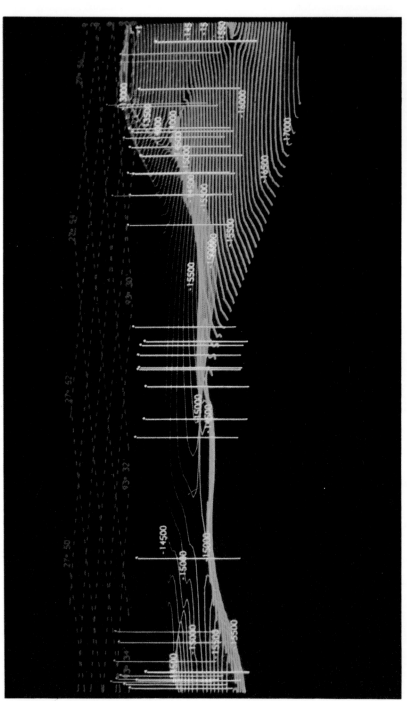

Figure 2-2. Example of a full-color, 3D display that is rotatable around an axis. Such capability enhances seismic data interpretation in a world with 3D relationships. (Courtesy, Evans and Sutherland.)

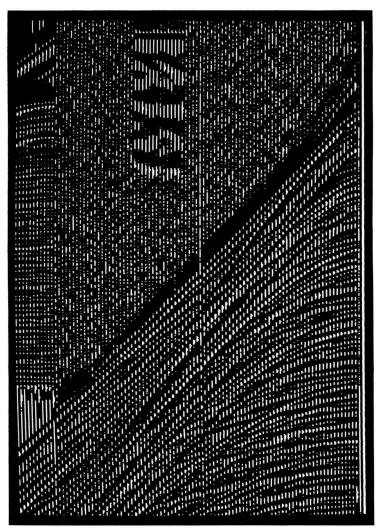

Figure 2-3. The seismic field record is displayed on a vector refresh graphics terminal. Seismic data displays require large amounts of trace data to be viewed simultaneously so that correlation between traces can be analyzed. (Courtesy Adage, Inc.)

map-oriented data base manager. They are the first step towards developing an interactive interpretation console. As more explorationists gain access to the new mini-computers, there will be a demand for software that allows for an easy exchange of information between users as well as between multi-level data base systems. With the new mini/micro-computer capabilities there should be a decentralized company computer network established. Local interpretation groups will need to buy computer time from a large scalar or vector main frame computer to handle large number-crunching problems.

It has yet to be shown conclusively that an interactive interpretation console would be accepted by interpreters, or that it is cost effective. A specific comparison of the efficiency and accuracy improvements of an interactive over a batch interpretation system needs to be made. Activities that are repetitive enough to be useful in this type of a test include velocity analysis, bright spot analysis, tying synthetic modeling to a seismic stratigraphy interpretation, ray trace modeling, etc.

This is why one of the major technologies requiring emphasis in the 1980s is data base management. System level computer-software-interpreters that will be able to extract information from present data storage systems will make all data files interactively available to explorationists. This will be the major improvement in data handling techniques and interactive interpretation in the 1980s. Coordination of these technologies allows the integration of seismic data with location maps, landsat, surface geology, potential data, well logs, geochemical information and with other large sets of exploration data.

CHANGE

There are changes in exploration methods occurring, although they are guaranteed to be slow and disruptive as change always is. The broad overview given here has been presented in an optimistic manner. Many of the new technologies discussed are tied to computers that realistically should be talked about with some pessimism.

Even more basic are problems of the computer language limitations. Geophysics is a science of surfaces, and yet we have tied ourself to a computer language, i.e., Fortran, that cannot communicate in terms of surfaces and maps. There must be reevaluation in some very basic areas.

Another problem is that of the super salesman. In attempting to get the best equipment, it is easy to end up with an unbalanced system, where there is no communications between different parts of the system. The super computers have the potential of running 1,000 times faster. However, if the software is not completely reworked and vectorized, the super computers will be less efficient than present scalar computers.

The business philosophy of centralized systems can often lead to large unwieldy bureaucracies that stagnate. However, there is a lack of control with distributed systems. New technologies must be tied to the business philosophy of each individual company.

Interpretation presents a good example of why change and acceptance of the new technologies has and will continue to be slow. Seismic interpreters have traditionally gone through an apprenticeship of five to ten years. Understanding how to extract geological information from seismic sections takes experience. The people that are good interpreters went through this apprenticeship. It is often hard to see how a machine can help substitute for experience. Confusion has diminished from the time computers first entered the market place. As procedures are shown to be truly effective, they will be incorporated.

TRAINING EXPLORATIONISTS

The biggest problem for oil and gas exploration in the 1980s is the shortage of well-trained explorationists. There are many scientists being attracted from related fields like physics, mathematics, and geochemistry. However, it takes several years to educate them in geology, processing techniques, data collection procedures, etc. There is tremendous competition for those who do have the training and any experience. Small companies are buying the best brains and experience available. The Houston division of one major oil company has had such a large personnel turnover that in mid-1981 more than half of the work force had not been with the company long enough to have earned vacation time. Universities and consulting firms throughout the world are taking steps to train more explorationists. With government funds drying up, one of the biggest boons to applied geophysical education and research has been the development of industry-sponsored research consortia. The impact of these groups is starting to be seen in the literature and in the job market. One mid-sized oil company is sponsoring at least 13 separate university research consortia.

The University of Houston is an example of one school that is attempting to meet this need for educating applied geophysicists. In 1977, Dr. Fred Hilterman in the Department of Geology and Dr. Keith Wang in the Department of Electrical Engineering organized one of these research groups to specifically study physical modeling and in general 3D seismic techniques.[15] They have since left the University of Houston, but the Seismic Acoustics Laboratory (SAL) continues under the direction of Dr. G.H.F. Gardner and Dr. John A. McDonald with the sponsorship of 43 major oil exploration companies (May, 1983). The SAL has been so successful that there has been a whole new organization formed to develop applied geophysical research and help train explorationists. This new organization is called the Allied Geophysical Laboratories (AGL) and presently consists of five separate research groups, with the SAL being the largest. AGL is an interdisciplinary enterprise being jointly endorsed and recognized by the departments of geoscience and electrical engineering.

Two grants of $500,000 each to the newly-named Department of Geosciences started two of the other groups. One grant, from the Cullen Foundation, has been used to help establish the Cullen Image Processing Laboratory. This lab is working on new ways to access the volumes of information in 3D surveys and ways to display and interact with this data. The equipment includes the two major vector refresh graphics systems, one with a raster segment generator, a true 3D display device, and some color raster graphics equipment.

The other grant, from the W.M. Keck Foundation (named for the late William Keck, Sr., founder of Superior Oil Co.), was used to purchase a VAX-based Digicon geophysical processing system. This computer system forms the basis for the Keck Research

Computation Laboratory. Thanks to a grant from CDC, this lab is also doing work on a CDC super computer in Minneapolis via Cybernet. The other labs are the Field Research Laboratory and the Well Logging Laboratory, which is in its third year under the Department of Electrical Engineering and has 16 sponsors.

The AGL is providing a synergistic forum for developing and expanding 3D seismic techniques. More importantly it, like other university research consortia, is providing hands-on training in modern exploration geophysics techniques for students from electrical engineering, geology, computer science, physics and other related fields of study.

SUMMARY

The new technological breakthroughs of the 1970s and 1980s are changing the methods of exploring for petroleum energy. Many of these changes are a result of computer technology, ranging from micro-computer developments to special configurations of mini-computers to the new super computers. These developments are greatly affecting data collection, all the way from surveying to recording technology. New methods for displaying and working with seismic data point to the possibility of interactive 3D interpretation. However, technology is not an answer to all exploration problems. In order for an impact to be made, these new developments need to be coupled with properly trained personnel to bring about smoother transitions. University applied research consortia are one of the best ways to develop the needed manpower to help solve the energy problem.

References

1. Arnason, B., Mobil Exploration and Producing Services, Inc., field operations, personal communication, 1981.
2. Martin, D. H., Cyberan, Inc., personal communication, 1982.
3. Gardner, G. H. F., "3D Seismic Techniques Introduction," SEG 3D Seismic Techniques School notes, Segment 1, 1979.
4. McDonald, J. A., "Design of Areal Collection Systems," SEG 3D Seismic Techniques School notes, Segment 7, 1979.

5. Rice, R. B., *et al*, "Developments on Exploration Geophysics, 1975-1980," *Geophysics*, V. 16, No. 8, pp. 1088-1099, 1981.
6. Kosloff, D. D., visiting professor of geophysics at Univesity of Houston, personal communications, 1981.
7. Dillahunty, R. C., Fash, J. L., Parsley, L. R., and Townsend, D. W., "Geo physical Data Bases: System Considerations," *Geophysical Prospecting*, V. 28 No. 4, pp. 495-512, 1980.
8. Bone, M. R., Giles, B.F., Tegland, E.R., "Seismic Data Analysis with Time Subcrop Techniques, " annual SEG meeting. Denver, Oct. 1975, (see also abstract, *Geophysics*, V. 41, No. 2, p.p. 342-343, 1976.
9. Nelson, H. R., Jr., Hilterman, F. J., Gardner, G. H. F., "Introduction to Inter-active 3D Interpretation, *"SEG Proceedings*, V. 1, pp. 415-458, 1980, (see also abstract, *Geophysics*, V. 46, No. 4, p. 409).
10. Sher, L. D., "The Space Graph Display: Principles of Operation and Application, "SAL *Semi-Annual Progress Review*, V. 5, pp. 212-224, 1980.
11. Johnson, S., and Brent B., "Utah 3D Volume Viewer a True 3D Display for Graphics Geophysical and Other Applications, "SAL *Semi-Annual Progress Review*, V. 5, pp. 225-232, 1980.
12. Jansson, D. G., Berlin, E. P., Jr., Straus, I., Goodhue, J. T., "A Three-Dimensional Computer Display," SAL *Semi-Annual Progress Review*, V. 7, pp. F8-25, 1981.
13. Ricks, D. E., "A New Interactive 3D Display Provides High Resolution Color Images," SAL *Semi-Annual Progress Review*, V. 7, pp. F41-48, 1981.
14. Simpson, A. L., "The Image Processing Lab: Status and Plans," SAL *Annual Progress Review*, V. 8, pp. 518-527, 1981.
15. Hilterman, F. J. , Nelson, H. R., Jr., Gardner, G. H. F., Offshore Technology Conference Proceedings "Physical Modeling: An Aid for Production Geophysicists," paper No. 4022, pp. 139-147, 1981.

CHAPTER 3

Multi-Channel Seismic Recording Systems

The trend towards more and more channels for seismic data collection is described in this chapter. The 1970s have led to the development of several new methods of simultaneously collecting seismic data with a large number of recording channels or seismic recording groups (up to 4,096). This chapter addresses those multi-channel geophysical recording systems that use telemetry data transmission methods. In addition, a system that stores data on cassette cartridges and some work in fiber optics transmission are described.

Is bigger better? Is a larger multi-channel recording system going to help a company find more oil and gas and do it more economically? This question has to be answered by each exploration manager, independently. Therefore, this chapter is aimed at providing a consolidated review of the frontier developments in multi-channel geophysical recording systems (1982) in order to help exploration-ists become more completely aware of the available options.

There can be major problems when recording systems grow too big or too complex. How is it possible to keep track of where each of a large number of recording stations are located? What keeps the right geophone/hydrophone station tied to the proper recording channel? How are the surveying or positioning difficulties associated with many recording stations overcome? What improvements come as a result of putting more recording stations out simultaneously? Can the problems associated with increased size be minimized so that the system is cost effective, even without considering improved data results.?

WHY MORE CHANNELS?

One of the most convincing reasons for larger numbers of active recording stations is that it is *less expensive to record the same amount of data.* The data collected with 1,000 recording positions covers more than ten times the surface area that a 96-channel crew does at each source position. A system with 384 channels will still provide four times the surface area or linear length coverage of a 96-channel crew per shot point or vibrator point. It does take longer to get 1,000 channels out on the ground than 96 channels, but with proper planning the movement of geophone stations along a line or over an area will go smoothly with either system. Monthly crew costs are estimated, on average, to be one-third more per month when one of the new, larger sytems is operated, and this is still less expensive per amount of data collected. However, there are higher crew start-up costs. One company had a start-up cost budget increase from $2 million to $3.5 million when comparing starting a 96-channel crew and new multichannel telemetry crew, respectively.

Data quality improvement is the second major factor favoring the new systems. More channels allow closer spacing of receiver stations, which helps preserve the continuity of reflection horizons, and accommodates longer spreads, which help distinguish between primary and multiple reflections.[1] There is improvement in the signal-to-noise ratio because of the increased redundancy or fold that can be obtained. A better handle of critical weathering statics corrections is obtained with more geophone stations. The larger number of channels also allows access to and proper data collection in remote or inaccessible land prospects.

Expanding the number of channels allows for the extension of coverage to areas instead of lines. This improves the spatial sampling of 3D (three-dimensional) geological structures and provides a better picture of the subsurface. (See Chapter 4 for a discussion of areal or 3D seismic collection techniques.)

A third argument for the new telemetry and cassette multichannel recording systems is that they are *environmentally sound.* In remote areas it is easier to run a long telemetry wire and set up a radio telemetry or cassette recorder than to cut a road for the recording truck. These systems are designed to be used on completely portable crews. However, as with all environmental protection, the final decision is in the hands of man. It requires common sense on the part of the crew not to leave trash, start fires, tear up roads or otherwise damage the terrain.

DATA TRANSMISSION

Parallel Systems

Present standard recording systems bring data from the seismic recording groups in parallel. In other words, there is a pair of wires from each geophone/hydrophone group that goes to a corresponding recording channel. These channels are the interface for putting the data on magnetic tape. For a standard land seismic crew, there are 96 channels in each cable coming into the recording truck. With a typical trace spacing of 220 to 440 feet per recording station and an average of 150 live stations on the ground, there are 6 to 12 miles of cable, with 96 pairs of wires, on the ground at one time. These wires are obviously subject to damage by any wildlife or vehicles. The cables are also heavy and hard to place.

Serial Systems

In contrast to parallel systems, serial data transmission relays the data from a group of recording stations one at at time.[2] Serial data transmission is often referred to as telemetry transmission, because the data from the recording stations are sent to the recording unit as a string of data. This is the same process as a radio transmission, only the signal travels along a 2-strand wire similar to the wire to a TV antenna. Therefore, a wire-line telemetry transmission of up to 1,024 recording stations would only have one pair of wires (as opposed to 96 pairs) connecting each recording station to the recording equipment. This allows for many more channels to be called with a small amount of wire out on the ground or in the marine cable. There is not even a need for wire connections to the recording unit if radio telemetry or cassette cartridges are used.

With the large number of channels that are being transmitted to the recording truck, there can be a significant time delay between each shot point. One radio telemetry system reports an average of 5 to 7 seconds total recording time for 4 channels. This means that if 1,000 channels were being recorded at once it would take between 20 and 30 minutes to get the data from one shot back to the recorder.

Another radio telemetry system estimates 10 seconds per channel, which means that for a 4,095-channel system it would take 11 hours to bring the data from one shot point back to the recording truck. This, of course, is not going to work in a field production environment.

MULTI-CHANNEL RECORDING

Marine Systems

There are two major vendors of marine telemetry systems: Digicon, Inc.[3] and Litton Resources Systems, Inc., [1,4,5] which is associated with Western Geophysical. As stated earlier, this book does not seek to compare the different systems or to make recommendations to which is the best to buy for any specific reason. Therefore, in writing about the capabilities of similar types of equipment of which the author is aware the discussion will not tie the equipment descriptions to a specific vendor.

The major component of telemetry digital streamer systems is the digitizing unit, which services 4 or 12 analog seismic hydrophone channels. One unit is described as being "incorporated into a neutrally-buoyant, corrosion-resistant titanium streamer section connector." These streamer digitization units are identical, or at the least have identical memory boards that can be easily interchanged for any required maintenance. Instead of sending analog signals down several hundred pairs of wires to parallel banks of amplifiers, digitizers and recording instruments on the ship, the A/D (analog-to-digital) conversion is accomplished in the streamer digitizing units.

One unit has at time-division multiplexing system that puts digital data from 12 data channels and 2 auxiliary channels into a coaxial line. Each module receives its own separate control instructions from the operator using a control system based on signal propagation time in the cable. Crews with 192 and 480 channel cables are currently in operation. On these crews each channel is sampled at a rate of 1 ms (millisecond). The other system records 120 seismic channels at 1 ms sample rate, or 240 channels with a 2 ms sample rate. The streamer depth is precisely monitored with individually controlled units called birds, and the depth (± 1.5 ft or 0.46 m) and bearing information ($\pm 0.35°$) is recorded between shots.

One of the major reasons for developing these telemetry marine seismic systems is to meet the need for increased resolution in the horizontal direction (more traces per unit cable length) and in the vertical direction (recording higher frequency seismic information). Closer trace spacing increases horizontal resolution by making reflection horizons more continuous. There are variable section lengths between modules to aid in horizontal resolution.

Vertical resolution is improved as higher frequencies are recorded. One-eighth of the wavelength of the highest frequency recorded is the minimum bed thickness that can be resolved with a seismic reflection system.[6] Therefore, the high-cut filter needs to be adjustable upwards to allow for the inclusion of higher frequencies, and the phase response of each hydrophone group has to be identical, so that combining them does not introduce frequency cancellation. The high-cut filter of one system can be telemetry selectable for frequencies 80, 160, or 320 Hz.

Land Systems

Three types of land telemetry systems, a cassette cartridge system, and fiber optics systems will be discussed in this section. The land serial recording equipment includes the wire line telemetry systems marketed by Gus Manufacturing and Sercel, the signbit GEOCOR IV wire line telemetry systems built by Geophysical Systems Corp., and the radio telemetry OPSEIS system marketed by Applied Automation, Inc. The system described as a surf zone system is built by Fairfield Industries. The SGR (Seismometer Group Recorder) cassette cartridge system is built and marketed by Gus Manufacturing. Fiber optics parallel transmission of full resolution data are being built or studies by several companies, including Geosource, Mark Products, and Professional Geophysics Inc.

Wire line telemetry systems that transmit 14 bits of data consist of remotely controlled boxes that collect, process, digitize, format and hold the data until the correct time slot for multiplexed transmission to the doghouse. In GUS-BUS terminology the Remote Data Acquisition Units are called RDAUs and the central recording unit a Line Interface Unit or an LIU.[7] Sercel calls the remote units Line Channel Boxes and the central unit a Sercel-SN 348.[8]

In one system the remote boxes have a clip that snaps around and breaks the twin-lead line insulation at any point one desires a station to be positioned. Thus, any group interval or spacing is feasible. Each of these remote boxes serves four receiver stations.

The other system has single channel boxes that are separated in the field by 100 meters or less. A field power supply box boosts the signal between every set of 40 remote units. The systems have been developed to provide automatic self checking of unit status, and one system allows remote checking of geophone strings from the recording truck. A low frequency pilot tone precedes the shot to power up the remote units from standby. It takes 2 seconds for the entire line to settle down after powering up. The 4-channel units have a 4-digit indicator for ground station number, and units are called up by station number addresses for each data gathering cycle. After the data cycle ends, the unit returns to standby.

The units have remotely controlled low-cut and notch filters. When the author visited a GUS-BUS crew, data was being collected under a long distance power transmission line; no interference was noted on the monitors, although crews have reportedly been shut down by high-line noise. If the line is inactive, a pocket-sized line communicator can be used to talk to the doghouse. The farthest unit can be 2 to 6 miles (3.2 to 9.7 km) from the recorder depending on environmental conditions. The 4-channel remote units weigh 27 lbs. (12 kg), with batteries, and are 16 in. by 7.5 in. by 13 in. (40.6 by 19.1 by 33.0 cm) in size. The single channel box weighs only 3 lbs. (1.4 kg).

Because these systems use a simple two-wire cable, there are drastic reductions in cable costs. This makes it operationally feasible to deploy hundreds of channels in two dimensions. As many as 50 individual 4-channel units may be connected to a single twin lead line, and the number of active units is limited only by the sample rate. Standard sample rates are 1, 2, or 4 ms. These systems can record up to 768 channels simultaneously. Typically, 10 miles

(16 km) of line (or 4, 10-mile lines) are used before moving the truck up. The one channel system can record up to 480 channels at a 4-ms sample rate. Some prospects, particularly 3D surveys over a known field, can be shot entirely from one setup. There are also automatic roll-a-long procedures for various line and areal data collection configurations.

Advertised accessories that are of interest include a 384-channel, solid-state compositor/demultiplexer that works with 16-second records that have a 1-ms sample rate "on the fly" (as fast as the data arrives at the box). Most vendors are building real-time correlators and stackers that are compatible with their systems. One company advertises an 8,000-bpi (bit per inch) tape drive that can be added to compatible systems. Another sells 6,250-bpi tape drives for simultaneously recording a group of 480 channels. These drives do not have a vacuum column, which is very useful, especially where there is a lot of dust.

Sign-bit wire line telemetry is marketed as GEOCOR IV by Geophysical Systems Corp (1982).[9] This system is able to simultaneously record and process 1,024 independent data channels at sample rates as small as 1/4 ms. Data processing includes demultiplexing, correlating and compositing all of the channels as the data acquisition proceeds using a high speed processor with three million, 16-bit words of solid state memory. A 512-fold, CDP (common depth point) stacked section can also be generated off-line at the crew site nightly. These capabilities allow field tests to be evaluated and modified and recording parameters to be regularly reset in the field to help improve data quality.

This system, like the wire line telemetry systems previously discussed, has a series of battery-operated boxes along the receiver spread. Each box controls the sampling and digitizing of data from 16 adjacent geophone channels. The data are transmitted to the recording truck in frames of serial data. Every frame is refreshed as it passes through successive terminals along the line so that the data can be transmitted long distances without being degraded.

The unique characteristic of the GEOCOR IV system is that only the polarity of the geophone signal is recorded. Positive polarities are noted with a 1 and negative polarities with a 0. Because the only numbers utilized are 0 and 1, and because this information can be recorded as one bit of data per time sample, the technique is called "sign-bit recording." It has been shown that accurate relative amplitudes can be recovered from the polarity information using cross-correlation, and high-fold CMP stacking. Synthetic tests at the Seismic Acoustics Laboratory (University of Houston) show that amplitude recovery of sign-bit data can be achieved by either stacking with a large fold (up to 480 was tested) or doing migration with a large enough aperture (100 traces were used).[10] The more traces that are added, the better the results. It has been argued that the need for higher fold and more spatially dense data requires that the same number of data bits be recorded as are recorded on a traditional 16-bit, 96-channel recording crew. However, sign-bit technology does work.

The data can be called from channels along a single line, or from up to 16 independent lines, as long as the total number of channels selected does not exceed 1,024. The recording truck can be placed at either end of a collection scheme or anywhere within the receiver stations to make the field operations more efficient. All operator communications take place through a CRT (cathode ray tube) with a standard keyboard using simple English. The system interrogates the operator for each parameter and checks the validity of each entry. This simplifies operation procedures and minimizes operator error.

Another capacity (some say requirement) of this system is the ability to vary the sweep frequencies between vibrator move-ups at the same shot point. High-speed correlation before compositing makes this possible with no delay in data acquisition. GeoSystems calls this proprietary technique Varisweep.[TM] This allows the operator to tailor the frequency spectrum to emphasize the frequencies that best define the reflection sequences of interest.[9]

Radio telemetry systems are built and marketed by Applied Automation[11] and Fairfield Industries.[12] Fairfield is field testing a system similar to the Applied Automation OPSEIS. Telseis II can theoretically record 4,095 channels called in blocks of 12 or 24 channels. However, Fairfield systems are best known for surf zone seismic recording, and will be discussed under that heading.

The OPSEIS radio telemetry system (Figure 3-1) is based on 4-channel digitizing boxes called Remote Telemetry Units (RTUs). Like the wire line telemetry systems, RTUs are portable units designed to work under the most adverse climatic and topographical conditions. They have an attachable floatation device so they

Figure 3-1. Observer talking to the recording truck from an OPSEIS Remote Telemetry Unit. These units are essentially four-channel, portable, digitizing boxes designed to relay seismic data without the use of wires. (Courtesy Applied Automation, Inc.)

can be used in swamps, lakes, or other water environments. The RTU weighs 38 lbs (17.2 kg) with the rechargable and removable battery pack and is 14 in. by 9 in. by 10 in. (35.6 by 22.9 by 25.4 cm). The batteries from a typical field layout can be charged overnight from a single 115-volt AC plug. A telescoping directional antenna mounted to the case is used for both transmitting and receiving. A phone can be plugged into the RTU for voice communication to the doghouse when there is no data being transmitted.

The microprocessor that controls the RTUs has 254 discrete addresses, which allows 1,016 receiver channels to be recorded for each shot. The observer's CRT display has 200-channel page displays; therefore, the system is normally referred to as having 5 pages or 1,000 channels available. The recording channels can be assigned in up to 10 separate lines for 3D spreads. It takes an average of 5 to 7 seconds total recording time for 1 box or 4 channels to be transmitted to the recording unit. This time includes a 3 to

5-second overhead in the central recorder to demultiplex the 4 channels and print out a 64-channel camera paper record. Because the recording equipment is completely portable and distributed in the field, a standard-sized recording truck seems very empty with just the OPSEIS recording control equipment in it.

The data are transmitted exclusively over an RF (radio frequency) link between the remote locations and the central recording station. A repeatable command and data checking techniques insure data integrity even under poor signal conditions. The RF link is within assigned FCC (Federal Communications Commission) frequency bands. Seismic data are transmitted by paging through the RTUs over an 8 to 15 mile distance (depending on terrain). A repeater is presently being field tested that will allow the recording unit to "see" over hills (1982). The systems are also being expanded to enable real time correlation in the doghouse and to allow the stacking of vibrator move-ups in the RTUs.

The cassette cartridge recording system is called the Seismometer Group Recorder (SGR, Figure 3-2), [13] and is built and marketed by Gus Manufacturing. Each SGR has a single channel that is recorded on a cassette cartridge for every shot or vibrator point. Theoretically, there is no limit to the number of channels that can be recorded using this system. In Wyoming, crews are being run with these systems that record 1,000 channels per shot point. The normal crew, doing non-3D data collection, will use 250 to 300 recording devices. Each tape holds little more than 160 six-second shot records on a standard 350-foot tape. There are 450-foot cassette cartridges available. The system is mostly used on shot crews, but it can be used with vibrators.

The cassettes are normally changed when the SGR is picked up as the line rolls along. When the box is located at the next station the location is noted with a dial on the box. The file number, record number, etc., are transmitted from the controlling point. The boxes are normally stored in 40 carrying racks on the back of a flat bed pickup. These racks have rechargers, for overnight recharging. Normally batteries are not replaced in the field, the dead unit is just replaced and recharged. At the end of the day the cassettes are dumped out onto 9-track, 1,600-bpi tapes at the crew office. This is done in a random order and the shots are put back in proper order in the home office as part of the preprocessing.

Figure 3-2. An SGR cassette cartridge system being placed in the field. A single channel is recorded on the tape for every shot or vibrator point. Data from the individual tapes are dumped onto a larger system at day's end.

Surf Zone Systems

The OPSEIS system previously described can be used for surf zone recording. However, the most commonly used system is Fairfield Industry's TELSEIS 200 (Figure 3-3).[12] It is set up so that each channel has a separate radio frequency. However, FCC regulations limit this to 66 channels in the U.S.; whereas, 96 channels are used overseas. This is different from the other telemetry systems that have been described because it records channels in parallel rather than serially. The system is designed to collect data in the "marine-to-land" gap. The telemetry units can be used continually as the spread progresses from land through swamp

Figure 3-3. A TELSEIS radio system at work in the field. Each channel utilized (up to a maximum of 66 channels in the U.S.) has a separate radio frequency. It can be operated from land or in shallow to deep water zones without equipment change. (Courtesy Fairfield Industries.)

and surf zones and into the deeper waters. No equipment changes are required for these different environments and the system can broadcast to a maximum of 30 miles.

Fiber Optics Systems

Fiber optics transmission will be used on parallel and not a telemetry seismic recording systems. Geosource has a 240-channel fiber optics system that records at a 4-ms sample rate, and was field tested during the summer of 1982. This system writes data on tape directly from the field using a variable speed tape drive. A similar system is being developed by Mark Products, Inc[14]. The Mark Products system has 8 input fiber optics lines, each of which can carry 1024 channels at a 4-ms sample rate. When these lines are paired to become 4 input strings, the system can record 4 × 1024 channels at a 2-ms sample rate. Each sample is recorded with 11 bits of resolution, 3 bits exponent, and the sign going directly into memory. By double-buffering the memory, they plan to be able to do demultiplexing in real-time using Intel 8086/88 micro-processor chips.

Besides the amount of data that can be recorded, fiber optics technology opens several other doors for field crews. A cable that is 1,700 ft. (520 m) long only weighs about 30 lbs (13.6 kg). This makes a tremendous difference in laying out a program in rough terrain. The Mark Products system has remote data units with 8 input channels. Like the other distributed systems described there can be problems in ensuring system integrity. For example, one of the biggest problems with any cable system is identifying and fixing breaks. It is possible to electronically measure within 1% accuracy (20 ft or 6 m) where a break is. Once a break is located, the cover can be opened, the fiber fused with a repair instrument, and shrink tubing put over the splice. There is about ½ db (decibel) loss of energy for each repair, and so a cable can only be repaired about twenty times before it is nonfunctional. Although there is still development work and field testing to be done, this is an exciting new technology in the area of seismic data acquisition.

RECORDING SYSTEMS

It is safe to project that the standard manufacturers of seismic recording systems will continue to increase the number of channels and the resolution of their equipment. The active development of the 32-bit DFS-V is an example. This Texas Instruments' recording unit handles up to 240 channels with a sample rate that can range from 0.5 to 4 ms.

Another parallel recording system is Litton Resources Systems' LRS-9, which can record up to 960 channels at 0.5 ms sample interval. This is a modular system with 64 channels in each data acquisition module. Every pair of channels has "channelized" data storage so that recording on magnetic tape is independent of acqu-isition rates. [15] The development of real-time correlators and com-positors will have a major impact on the future production of standard parallel data acquisition systems.

New memory and electronics developments, in general, promise to further revolutionize acquisition systems. A list of some of the developments just over the horizon includes: all power coming from the truck and at lower level, full 132-decibel dynamic range with no gain ranging, telemetry units that only weigh a few ounces per trace, repeaters designed to build up a signal as it travels down the cable, field-tested fiber optics data transmission systems, laser light as a communication link instead of wire or radio telemetry, bubble memories tied to portable recording systems, video discs for very high-density field recording systems and satellite communication systems for telemetering data from an unlimited number of stations back to a central processing center. The future of reflection seismology multichannel acquisition systems is limited only by the imagination of today's explorationists.

SUMMARY

The new developments in multichannel telemetry seismic systems are starting to have a major impact on the methods of exploration for petroleum energy. The multichannel systems range from wireline telemetry crews (marine and land) to radio telemetry systems (land and surf zone) to multiple, single-channel boxes that record data on cassette cartridges. Simultaneously, traditional parallel recording systems are rapidly increasing in the number of channels. They are also taking advantage of new electronic and communication developments like fiber optics data transmission. There are many new technologies that need to be further developed and the future promises many more changes in data acquisition systems.

References

1. Savit, C. H. and Siems,L. E., "A 500-Channel Streamer System," preprint of presentation given at the OTC, 1977.
2. Nelson, R., Inseis Control Inc., personal communication, 1981.
3. "DSS-240 Micropower Digital Streamer System," Digicon, Inc., brochure, 1981.

4. Siems, L. E., Litton Resources Systems, Inc., "Marine Seismic Systems with Large Numbers of Channels," preprint of presentation given at the 49th annual international SEG meeting, New Orleans, 1979 (see also abstract, *Geophysics*, V. 45, No. 4, pp. 518, 1980.)

5. "LRS-16 Marine Telemetry System," Litton Resources Systems brochure, 1979.

6. Widess, M. B., "How Thin is a Thin Bed?," *Geophysics*, V. 38, No. 6, pp. 1176-1180, 1973.

7. "GUS-BUS Digital Seismic Telemetry System," Gus Manufacturing brochure, 1980.

8. Miller, S., Sercel, personal communication, 1981.

9. "GEOCOR IV, 1024-Channel Seismic Data Acquisition and Processing System," Geophysical Systems Corp. brochure, 1981.

10. Hu T. and Gardner, G. H. F., "Migration and Stacking of Sign-Bit Seismic Data," SAL *Semi-Annual Progress Review*, V. 7, pp. N-1-37, 1981.

11. "OPSEIS 5500 System," Applied Automation brochure, 1981.

12. "TELSEIS," Fairfield Industries brochure, 1981.

13. Broding, R. A., "The Seismometer Group Recorder System," 44th annual international SEG meeting, Dallas, 1974 (see also abstract, *Geophysics*, V. 40, No. 1, p. 130, 1975).

14. Amason, J.M., Mark Products U.S., Inc., personal communication, Houston, Texas, 1982.

15. Shave, D.G., A Trace-Sequential Seismic Recording System with Effectively Unlimited Capacity," preprint of presentation given at the 49th annual international SEG meeting, New Orleans, 1979 (see also abstract, *Geophysics*, V. 45, No. 4, p. 518, 1980).

CHAPTER 4

3D Seismic Techniques

Three-dimensional (3D) seismic techniques are rapidly becoming more acceptable as a geophysical exploration tool, especially as a tool for field development. This chapter reviews the procedures for 3D seismic data collection, processing and interpretation used in both land and marine environments.

Three-dimensional seismology has been established as a viable geophysical exploration method over the last five years. There have been more than two hundred 3D seismic surveys shot during this time over both land and marine projects. These surveys have covered a variety of land environments ranging from the arctic to jungles, and from shallow water marshes to the Rocky Mountains; however, a majority of the surveys have been marine.

Seismic reflection surveys are normally carried out to solve a three-dimensional geologic problem. It is only logical to solve these problems with data sets that fill a 3D volume, rather than relying on 2D vertical seismic sections as has been historically done. With a 3D volume of data, traditional vertical seismic sections can be generated along any azimuth or direction (Figure 4-1). This allows evaluation of seismic data between wells, or along arbitrary directions that define critical geologic dip or closure. Horizontal seismic sections can also be generated from this data volume.

Probably more than half of the 3D surveys through 1981 were associated with field development projects.[1] The 3D method provides a sufficiently accurate and detailed picture of the subsurface to be economically attractive in developing a field. There are two

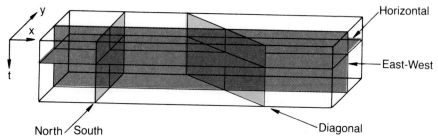

Figure 4-1. A 3D data volume allows for a much more complete evaluation of the subsurface. The data can be vertically sliced in any arbitrary direction to allow interpretation along the lines critical to an accurate evaluation. Horizontal sections can also be generated from a data volume.

primary ways that the procedure is proving to be economical. The first is to shorten the time between a discovery and subsequent production. The second cost savings comes in the ability to reduce the number of development wells by using a 3D seismic survey to allow more accurate well placement and to avoid dry holes. Also, untested fault blocks are frequently identified. The tradeoff in cost of 3D seismic versus development wells is documented in Table 4-1.[2]

3D ACQUISITION

Collection Design

Design of areal data collection systems can cover as many methods as the explorationists' ingenuity and the number of channels will allow. The distribution of source and receivers over an area instead of along a line, as in multifold profiling, squares the possible trace locations.

When data are collected over an area, there are specific locations for the source and the receiver. The midpoint between a specific source and receiver combination is referred to as a CMP (common midpoint) in this book. The four variables defining areal data are the CMP latitude and longitude coordinates, the offset from source to receiver and the azimuth of the offset. Linear profiling, on the other hand, usually has only two defining variables, a CMP location number and the offset distance.[3]

The two most common methods of 3D acquisition are parallel *CMP profiles* and *cross-spreads*. The most straightforward method is

Table 4-1
The Trade-off: 3D Seismic vs. Wells[2]

Area	Dry Development Well Cost* ($K)	3D Seismic Cost/Square Mile ($K)
Peru	2,000-3,000	30-40
North Sea	2,000-4,000	30-40
Gulf of Mexico	1,200-1,800	25-30
Alaska Land	2,000-2,500	50-80
U.S. Lower 48	700-1,000	35-50

*Well cost based on 10,000 ft. depth.

the collection of a set of closely spaced parallel lines, which is most common with marine 3D surveys. If there are strong cross currents when these surveys are collected, the deflection of the cable from the planned survey line can be much larger than the spacing between the lines. This problem can be solved by using a cable with a set of digital compasses to compute the location of each hydrophone group for each shot.[4]

The simplest geometrical representation of all other types of 3D seismic surveys is the *T-spread* (Figure 4-2), which consists of a line

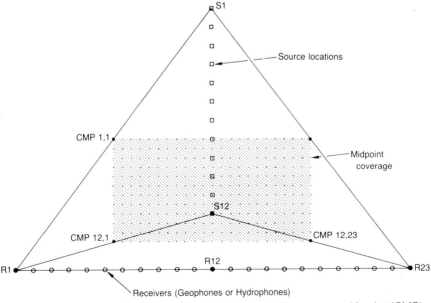

Figure 4-2. Cross-spread or T-spread data collection provides common mid-point (CMP) traces that cover an area. The T-spread is the simplest reduction of a 3D collection scheme, and can be expanded by running the receivers or sources in any arbitrary direction.

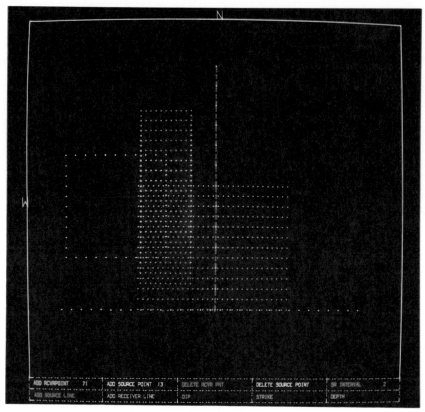

Figure 4-3. A map or aerial view of shot and receiver positions for a typical 3D survey shows the spatial relationship to generated CMP's. The shot points are marked in red along the vertical part of the X-spread. Receiver locations are marked in white, and are along both arms of the X-spread, as well as on the perimeter of a small square off to the north-west. The CMP's fall in between and are color coded by offset. (Courtesy Geosource, Petty-Ray Geophysical Division.)

of receivers and a perpendicular line of sources. The CMP's cover an area half of that defined by multiplying the source line length by the receiver line length. It is important to note that each CMP has a different offset, and so a different NMO (normal moveout) correction is required for each trace. This can be illustrated in 3D on an E & S vector refresh graphics system (Figures 4-3, 4-4). Users may interactively evaluate the fold, offset, and other parameters of a proposed 3D survey using the graphics technologies illustrated by these figures.

A *cross-spread* is an extension of the T-spread where the source and the receiver lines cross. Cross-spreads have been used for

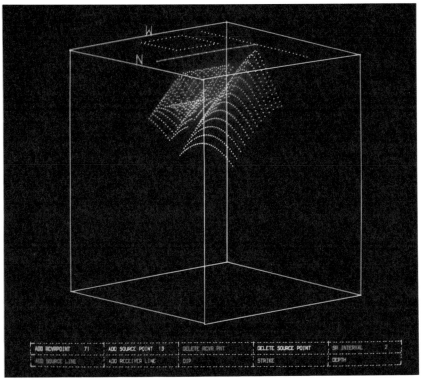

Figure 4-4. The offset differences for different CMP's are visually enhanced when the same information is displayed with offset shown as a function of required NMO correction along the z-axis. With an interactive display device, it is easy to rotate, translate, or scale this display to any desired orientation. (Courtesy Geosource, Petty-Ray Geophysical Division.)

marine work, but are generally used on land where the cost of parallel line profiling is too high and the necessary access is often denied. Normally, several parallel lines of geophones can be used to record each shot simultaneously. The overlapping of cross-spreads results in multifold data for each CMP (Figure 4-5). The cost of these surveys is reduced by increasing the number of channels recorded per shot. With over 500 channels per shot, the cost of 3D and 2D acquisitions are about equal.[3]

A further generalization of the T-spread is to place the receivers in a square or a loop and to shoot at stations around the square or loop. The advantage is that both in-line CDP data and areal data are collected. The multifold in-line data can be used to estimate static corrections and velocities, using standard programs, while the areal data sample the interior of the loop.

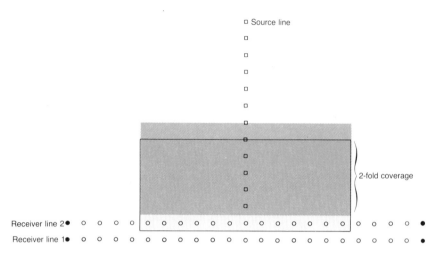

Figure 4-5. By shooting multiple source lines into the same receiver array, any desired CMP redundancy can be achieved. In the example above there is 2-fold coverage in the overlapped area and single fold coverage elsewhere. When there are two traces with different offsets at the same CMP, the data is referred to as 2-fold. Most 2D data collected today is 24, 48 or 96-fold, and by adding this redundant data together it improves the signal-to-noise ratio.

Although it is desirable to keep source and receiver lines straight and perpendicular to each other when collecting areal data, it is more important to place them so that the generation and detection of the signals will be reliable and repeatable. The most generally known example of this is G.S.I.'s Seisloop™. An example of this type of data collection is where receivers are placed along roads surrounding an inaccessible area of interest. As seismic sources are activated around this perimeter, CMP trace locations are generated that cover the area inside the loop. A set of bins are defined, and all of the traces that are spatially located in one of these bins are processed as being at the same CMP. By proper planning, a set of these data volumes can be put together to provide seismic coverage over an otherwise inaccessible area. Access may be denied to a specific area of interest for reasons varying from culture, to topography, to vegetation, to a lack of permits.

Missing shots or receivers will remove a row or a column from the CMP trace location grid. Isolated gaps will have no appreciable effect on the results. However, if the data are not sampled densely enough over the area or in time, there can be spatial or temporal aliasing. Aliasing, a loss of frequency information, occurs when there are less than two samples per cycle; thereby an input signal at a high frequency results in output at a lower frequency. For a 330-ft (100-m) surface receiver sampling interval (165 ft or 50 m sub-surface), and a 30 Hz signal, spatial aliasing will occur for dips over about 30 degrees. As a general rule in 3D data acquisition, it is better to place the receiver groups and shot arrays closer together than is customary for in-line work and to have a smaller fold. Land surveys with shot and receiver spacings of 80ft (25 m) have been successfully executed.

Surveying

Accurate surveying is critical in collecting a useable 3D data volume. The purpose of the surveying is to determine (x,y) coordinates and elevations for every source and receiver station, to tie this information the corresponding CMP seismic trace, and to relate the (x,y) coordinates to fixed geographic markers.[3] Although straight-forward, this is often one of the hardest steps to properly plan and efficiently carry out. In a typical 3D survey there may be several thousand stations and several million traces. Despite the many improvements in surveying techniques (Chapter 2), this is still a major problem for many 3D surveys.

In order to relate the location information to each CMP trace it is helpful to decide on an indexing scheme. For example, each station can be indexed by the source number on a named source line, and the receiver number on a named receiver line. If these indices are recorded on magnetic tape along with the coordinates and eleva-tions, then the order of the traces on the tape is not important. This has been found to work well in practice.[3]

Source/Receiver Arrays

Receiver arrays can be designed to efficiently attenuate surface waves and air waves along a 2D line. However, it is much more difficult to design effective 3D receiver arrays that can be used in the field. Point receiver stations have provided excellent processed results for 3D data sets.[3] It is also much easier logistically to do the "jug hustling" (placement and retrieval of the geophones) with point receiver stations. Data from point receiver stations can be combined in different manners during processing to remove the noise trains.

Theoretically, the results are the same as having source/receiver arrays in the field (although a few "old-timers" don't believe it until they see direct comparisons). This is one major reason why it is better to use as many active recording channels as possible, as discussed in Chapter 3. By using a 1,000-channel crew, a multi-arm cross-spread can be set out with receiver stations close enough together to allow 3D receiver array simulation in the computer. When a survey is being done in a new area, it is good to do some standard field noise test studies. It is also useful to be able to do some processing in the field in order to evaluate the noise attenuation.

PROCESSING 3D DATA SETS

The volume of data produced by a 3D survey is staggering. A 48-fold marine survey with 125 lines each having 100 shotpoints and recording 5 seconds of 4-ms data results in 7.5×10^8 digital samples, each a 32-bit word, which equals 2.4×10^{10} bits of data. The processing produces an output of about 5×10^8 bits. Each of these output bits results from thousands of manipulations during the processing steps.

The need to handle large amounts of data quickly in seismic processing has been a major motivating force in the development of the modern array processors and the new super vector computers. The increase in the number and size of 3D seismic surveys is certain to have additional impact on the future development of computer technology along with the economics accompanying energy crises.

Processing

Seismic processing of 3D data sets includes all of the processing steps required in standard 2D work. However, there are some additional problems that must be addressed in 3D work, starting with the amount of data that has to be handled simultaneously. In addition, it is important that there is sufficient multifold coverage for accurate velocity analysis and statics corrections. This can be accomplished with cross-spreads by shooting a standard multifold line along lines of receivers, or by laying out receivers along the source line for a multifold line along the direction of shooting.

The three issues of statics, velocity and migration are critical for successfully processing a 3D survey. *Statics* are the time shifts in data due to near surface velocity changes caused by weathering, permafrost, etc. The redundancy of large-fold CMP data can be used to reduce the uncertainty of statics estimates. Statics can have a major impact on velocity estimates and the choice of velocity affects the migration or focusing of the data.

Defining the proper *velocity* is of central importance to both stacking and migration. The velocities used in these two processes are normally different. Stacking velocities are related to NMO analysis of the reflection events in CMP gathers (groups or bias). Normal moveout is the correction that needs to be applied to the CMP traces located in the same bin or spatial location, which have different offsets. Once these traces are NMO corrected, they can be added together or stacked to improve the signal-to-noise ratio. Stacking velocities depends on layer velocity and interface dip, while migration velocities are independent of the dip of the reflecting surface.[5]

Migration is a focusing procedure that moves data into a proper position in space. The removal of fault diffractions are an example of the focusing accomplished using a standard 2D migration algorithm. Because seismic waves in the earth propagate in 3D and subsurface geology is 3D, vertical sections normally show energy from outside the plane. It has been clearly shown that 3D migration is necessary to construct accurate vertical profiles.[6]

The full 3D migration of a volume of seismic data requires that all of the data within the radius of the migration aperture be available for the computation of each output trace. The simultaneous storage and manipulation of this many traces is complicated and requires tremendous computer power. One simplification is to do a 3D migration in two steps, each step consisting of a 2D migration.[7] This reduces the computation effort from N^2 traces to 2N, and simplifies the necessary data handling when the Kirchhoff-summation method is used. The two-step method fails to produce the same results as a full single-pass 3D migration when the medium velocity is not constant, but the error usually does not seriously affect the interpretation. Another "simplification" is to transform

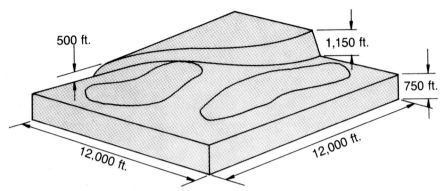

Figure 4-6. Three-dimensional physical or theoretical models, like SALGLF, provide a method of learning what to look for in a 3D field survey. The synthetic data collected over such a model can also be used to test 3D processing algorithms.

the data into the frequency domain, split the migration into parallel operations for different frequencies, and then combine the migrated results.[8]

Modeling of the problem synthetically or using physical scaled models can greatly aid in evaluating the success of the 3D processing, as well as in testing a proposed field layout or checking an interpretation Figure 4-6).[6,9,10] For example, migration of a 2D line that runs obliquely across a simple basin model produces an apparent fault.[11] True 3D migration would image the basin accurately. This is further discussed in Chapter 6. Work done by Gulf Oil pointed out that areal seismic processing techniques for detecting reefs were considerably aided by making use of experimental model data.[12]

3D INTERPRETATION

Interpretation methods have had to change to meet the quantity of data associated with a 3D survey. These changes are still happening and cover a wide range of techniques.

For example, a display box is used that has many vertical profiles on film. The interpreter will pull out a section of interest and mark it, then place the section back in 3D space to see how well the interpretation fits the other data. Reflection holography has also been ued to display data, although, because it is a photographic process, once displayed this data cannot be changed or interpreted. One of the best ways of working with 3D data sets is with animated movies of horizontal sections. These movies can be tied to an interpretation table so that as the sections are stepped through the interpreter can stop the movie at specific time intervals, and build a contour map.[13]

Horizontal sections have been shown to be worthwhile interpretation aids.[12] Most of the released examples come from the seismic contractors, one example being shown in Figure 4-7. Coloring the complex attributes of the seismic traces on horizontal sections give another dimension of understanding.

Interactive Display

Computer graphics is destined to play a major role in allowing interpreters to interactively evaluate the importance of frequency, amplitude, phase, polarity, velocity, or other trace attribute information. It is worthwhile to note that at least ten times more of the subsurface can be displayed using horizontal rather than vertical sections with the same number of CRT pixels (cathode ray tube picture elements). This is because traces are separated by a much larger distance than the space represented between time samples along a seismic trace.[14]

Display technology has improved to the point where it can be used for interactive interpretation of 3D data volumes (Figure 4-8).[15, 16, 17] This is an area where there is presently a lot of development taking place. It is reasonable to project that within a few years most interpretation groups will have access to some form of interactive interpretation workstation (Chapter 9). The merging of this technology with data base management systems that provide interaction between landsat, geochemical, potential, well-logs and surface geology data sets is not very far over the horizon (Chapter 10). When these developments are tied to real time 3D migration and velocity analysis, 3D interpretation techniques will catch up to the tremendous advances that have occurred in data collection, processing procedures, and hardware.

(text continued on page 109)

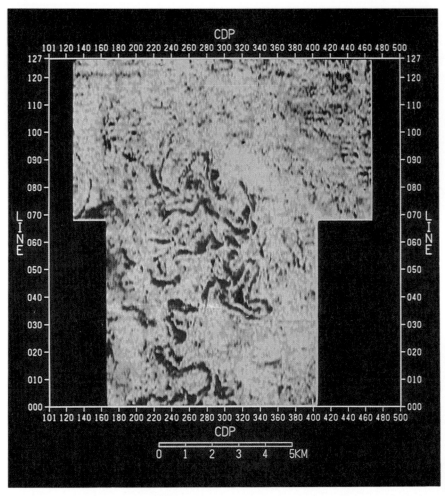

Figure 4-7. *The unique capabilities to interpret a subsurface geologic sequence with 3D data volumes is shown by this horizontal (SEISCROP) seismic section slicing a meandering stream channel in the Gulf of Thailand. (Courtesy Geophysical Service, Inc.)*

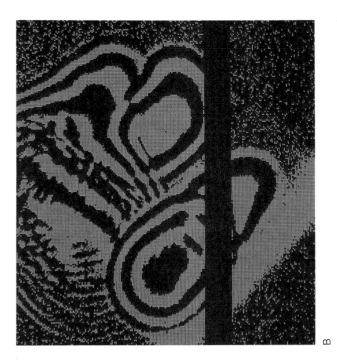

Figure 4-8. Interactive 3D interpretation techniques are becoming much more common. Here two horizontal sections across the SALGLF model are shown (A and B). There is no data in the black strip because of a data collection error.

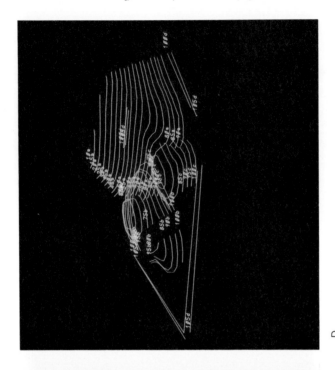

D

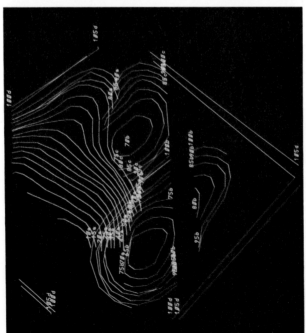

C

Figure 4-8 (continued). As horizontal sections are stepped through, they can be interactively interpreted as a 3D contour map that can be rotated in 3D space in real time (C and D).

SUMMARY

Three- dimensional seismic techniques have been established as a viable geophysical exploration tool. The most common use of the procedures described is in field development. However, these techniques are being used to define wildcat drilling locations by some companies. The extension of seismic data to cover areas brings it into better conformance with other exploration data, such as geological, geochemical, potential, remote imaging or topographic data. Because of its limited use, 3D seismic techniques can still be considered a new technology. Therefore, there are many changes and improvements presently being developed in acquisition, processing, and, especially, interpretation procedures.

References

1. Brown, A. R., and McBeath, R. G., "3D Seismic Surveying for Field Development Comes of Age," *Oil & Gas Journal,* Nov. 17, 1980, V. 78, No. 46, pp. 63-65, 1980.
2. Graebner, R. J., Steel, G. and Wason, C. B., "Evolution of Seismic Technology Into The 1980s," *A.P.E.A. Journal,* V. 20, Part 1, pp. 110-120, 1980.
3. Gardner, G. H. F., "3D Seismic Techniques Introduction," SEG 3D *Seismic Techniques School notes,* Segment 1, 1979.
4. McDonald, J. A., "Design of Areal Collection Systems," SEG 3D *Seismic Techniques School notes,* Segment 7, 1979.
5. Larner, K. and Gibson, B., "Subsurface Imaging Principles and Practice," SEG 3D *Seismic Techniques School notes,* Segment 5, 1979.
6. French, W. S., "Two-Dimensional and Three-Dimensional Migration of Model-Experiment Reflection Profiles," *Geophysics,* V. 39, No. 3, pp. 265-277, 1974.
7. Gibson, B., Larner, K. L., Solanki, J. J. and Ng, A.T.Y., "Efficient 3-D Migration in Two Steps," preprint of presentation given at the 41st annual meeting of the E.A.E.G., Hamburg, Germany, May, 1979 (see also abstract, *Geophysical Prospecting,* V. 27, No. 3, pp. 678-679, 1979).
8. Gardner, G. H. F., University of Houston Allied Geophysical Laboratories, personal communication, 1982.
9. Hilterman, F. J., "Interpretative Lessons from Three-Dimensional Modeling," preprint of presentation given at the 46th annual international SEG meeting, Houston, Texas, 1976 (see also abstract, *Geophysics,* V. 42, No. 1, p. 156, 1977).

10. Hilterman, F. J., Nelson, H. R. Jr., and Gardner, G. H. F., "Physical Modeling: An Aid for Production Geophysicists,"Offshore Technology Conference Proceedings, paper No. 4022, pp. 139-147, 1981.
11. Liang, L. C., and Hilterman, F. J., "2D Seismic Migration Effects from 3D Geological Structures," Offshore Technology Conference proceedings, paper No. 4096, pp. 263-269, 1981.
12. McDonald, J. A., Gardner, G. H. F. and Kotcher, J. S., "Areal Seismic Methods for Determining the Extent of Acoustic Discontinuities," *Geophysics*, V. 46, No. 1, pp. 2-16, 1981.
13. Brown, A. R., "3-D Seismic Interpretation Methods," preprint of presentation given at the 48th annual international SEG meeting, San Francisco, (see also abstract, *Geophysics*, V. 44, No. 3, p. 383, 1979).
14. Nelson, H. R., Jr., Hilterman, F. J. and Gardner, G. H. F., "Introduction to Interactive 3D Interpretation," *Oil & Gas Journal*, V. 79, No. 40, pp. 106-125, 1981.
15. Rice, G. W., Stebens, B. B. and Hall, P. M., "Interactive Color Display and Analysis—an Added Dimension to Seismic Interpretation," presentation given at the 51st annual international SEG meeting, Los Angeles, Calif., 1981 (see also abstract, *Geophysics*, V. 47, No. 4, p. 469, 1982).
16. Massell, W. F., Winningham, D. J. and Nelson, H. R., Jr., "Interactive Geophysical Analysis with 3D Color Graphics," presentation given at the 51st annual international SEG meeting, Los Angeles, Calif., 1981 (see also abstract, *Geophysics*, V. 47, No. 4, p. 469, 1982).
17. Nelson, H. R., Jr., Gardner, T. N. and Hilterman, F. J., "Interpretation of Physical Model Tank Data with the Raster Segment Generator," presentation given at the 51st annual international SEG meeting, Los Angeles, Calif., 1981 (see also abstract, *Geophysics*, V. 47, No. 4, pp. 497-498, 1982).

CHAPTER 5

Vector Computers

This chapter is an introduction to and a layman's summary of the needs for, architecture of and expected uses of the new vector computers in exploration geophysics. Array processors that perform specialized number crunching tasks have been tied to most geophysical processsng systems for the last 10 years. However, the use of vector computers in seismic data processing is just beginning to be tested and put on-line in the largest of the major oil companies and seismic contractors. The $10-to $20-million price tag has something to do with this. The use of these vector machines further requires a complete rethinking and reworking of seismic processing packages in order to effectively use parallel processing techniques. This means there is an extended learning curve before these systems will provide cost effective increases in processing speed. Major areas of expected application of this technology in exploration geophysics are summarized.

Computation requirements for geophysical processing have historically increased at least as fast as the development of new computer technologies. The need for increased processing power is the result of two major factors: the sheer volume of data that is being collected today, and the new processing algorithms or procedures that require instant access to larger portions of the data volume being evaluated.

Recent developments in multichannel recording systems[1] and in 3D (three-dimensional) seismic acquisition techniques[2] have greatly increased the amount of data that is being collected. For example, a 24-channel shothole crew will collect on the order of 24

× 10⁶ bits of information per day.* While about 300 × 10⁶ bits of information will be collected by a 48-channel Vibroseis℠ crew.† Recording 32-bit words for higher dynamic range and using 3D recording procedures, a 120-channel Vibroseis℠ crew will result in collection of about 1.250 × 10⁹ bits of information per day.‡ The daily amount of data collected by a 1,024-channel sign-bit Vibroseis℠ crew will average around 400 × 10⁶ bits of information. §

One of the biggest factors in the amount of seismic data being collected is the tremendous worldwide increase in the number of seismic reflection crews that has accompanied the realization of an energy crisis. In April 1976, there were 240 reflection seismic crews active in U.S. waters. By December 1981, this had increased to 704 active seismic crews.[3] Although the number of active crews worldwide fell in 1982, there is a trend toward more channels per crew and an obvious move towards 3D seismic techniques.

The processing of 3D seismic volumes typifies the requirements for new processing algorithms (mathematical procedures) that need instant access to larger portions of available data sets. When a volume of seismic data has a full 3D migration algorithm applied to it, all of the data within the radius of the migration aperture needs to be available for computing each output trace.[4] However, on a smaller scale, similar needs occur when CMP (common midpoint) gathers from two or three crossing lines are concurrently used to perform, for example, a 3D velocity analysis. When each data value is manipulated serially at every step of the algorithm, it can take a remarkably long time to evaluate even a modest volume of data.

SCALAR COMPUTERS

The processing used by almost all computer sytems today is serial or scalar. The four steps needed to multiply two numbers is a

---

* 50 shots/day × 24 channels/shot × 5 seconds/channel × 250 samples/second × 16 bits/sample = 24 × 10⁶ bits/day
† 100 vibrator points/day × 48 channels/V.P. × 16 seconds × 250 samples/second × 16 bits/sample = 307 × 10⁶ bits/day
†† 80 vibrator points/day × 120 channels/V.P. × 16 seconds × 250 samples/second × 32 bits/sample = 1.229 × 10⁹ bits/day
§ 100 vibrator points/day × 1024 channels/V.P. × 16 seconds × 250 samples/second × 1 bit sample = 410 × 10⁶ bits/day

good example of how a scalar computer works. These steps are to scale the first number, then scale the second number, then multiply the mantissas, and finally adjust the exponent.[5] When there are thousands of serial multiply and add statements that are applied to each trace, it can add up to a lot of computer time.

One way that the bottleneck inherent in scalar processing is overcome is to build electronic black boxes that sidetrack the problem. These systems are the various forms of array processors. They are designed to do repetitive operations on large numerical arrays, like a seismic trace, quickly, and where possible to do more than one operation at the same time. When an array processor multiples an array of numbers by one number, the array is fed into a pipeline. The first number of the array goes through the standard serial steps. However, as this number moves to the next step, another number follows it into the pipeline. One the pipeline is full, there is one multiplication result coming out for each processing step or clock cycle. This can result in significant time savings when doing repetitive operations on these long numerical arrays.

Array processors also have the capability to do several operations in parallel with one instruction. A typical example is to use one program statement simultaneously to do a floating point addition, a memory read, a floating point multiplication, and an integer addition (bumping a counter).[5] In order to use the array processors efficiently the large arrays have to be programmed so they will be recognized as vectors. It is an important step for the processor to recognize these arrays as vectors. The application for arithmetic and logical operations to vectors is known as vector processing.

VECTOR COMPUTERS

The new super vector computers can be grossly described as giant array processors. A more accurate portrayal is to describe these sytems as a combination of a host and a task processor. They have the same capabilities for pipeline and parallel processing. However, the machine controls automatically which operations are done in scalar mode and which statements are done in vector mode. The same logic that says that a computer-contolled multi-processing environment is more efficient than a single-job processing mode applies to this aspect of vector computers. Many operations appear to the user to be performed in a serial fashion, with other operations being performed in a parallel mode, but all operations are issued to strict sequence from a single instruction stream. The parallel or vector processing mode allows the manipulation of many operands (something, as a quantity or data, that is operated on, as in a mathematical operation) by a single instruction as discussed above. The operating system permits functional concurrency wherever possible while retaining the logical soundness of the user's program.[6]

A good example of parallel processing capabilities is the program loops that occur so often in scientific and geophysical processing. The pervasive nature of program loops has resulted in hardware and software designs that make it convenient for assembly language/machine language programmers to code program loops. Higher language loop structures, like the Fortran 'DO' statement, play a central role in geophysical processing. These loops can often be represented in terms of algebraic operations performed on linear lists (vectors) of operands. The vector computer takes advantage of the repetitious, similar computations involved in such loops by overlapping various stages of the computation.[7] This is accomplished in a similar manner to the pipeline processing discussed above.

One major advantage of vector processing over scalar processing is the elimination of overhead associated with maintenance of the loop control variable. Often these loops reduce to a simple sequence of instructions without backward branching. However, not all aspects of a problem lend themselves to vector processing. Scalar techniques still need to be applied to effectively do branching, as in a computed 'GO TO' statement. Consequently, the large vector machines provide both a scalar and a vector processor, with instructions and registers for both applications.[6, 8]

Seismic Processing

Seismic processing has had a major impact on the development of vector processing. For example, by the early 1960s the need for a rapid convolution method, or procedure to locate a given pattern on a seismic trace, was defined. The petroleum industry therefore sponsored the development of "convolver boxes." The main idea was to access the data as little as possible and maximize the arithmetic performed during each access. By the late 1960s these boxes had developed into the first floating point convolvers. The similarity of the convolution product algorithm to most other algorithms of linear algebra generated research and development of more generally applicable array processors.[9] By the beginning of the 1970s various seismic contractors and major oil companies had better defined their needs and had worked with hardware manufacturers to develop 32-bit systems for seismic and 64-bit systems for reservoir modeling, where rounding error requires more precision.[10] These systems developed and featured convolution, matrix multiplication, FFTs (fast Fourier transforms), recursive filtering and a variety of simpler algorithms.

By 1974, when CDC (Control Data Corp.) introduced the STAR-100, array processors in seismic data processing were well accepted. This was one of the first examples of an integrated scalar and vector processor. Around this same time, Seymour Cray, one of CDC's top computer designers, left CDC and the competing super vector computers of today began to be developed.

System Architecture

Architecture is quite different for the Cray and Cyber vector processing systems. However, it is not the purpose of the author to directly compare the sytems or to make recommendations as to which is the best to buy for any specific reason. Therefore, in writing about the capabilities of similar types of equipment of which the author is aware, the descriptions will not be tied to one vendor or the other. The different vector processing systems and their associated models cover a wide range of specifications.

The manner in which vectors are processed is a major difference between the Cray and Cyber systems. One system loads each vector into a vector register and then adds this to another vector register. This is theoretically a better way to work with short vectors, but also gives good results for long vectors. The other vector processor uses memory-to-memory streaming. This requires additional startup time to fill the pipes, but works extremely well on longer vectors, like a seismic trace. New models with greater capabilities are being tested regularly by both vendors.

Real memory in vector processors normally ranges up to 1 million 64-bit words. However, this can go as high as 32 million 64-bit words. One system has this memory arranged in 16 banks with a bank cycle time of 4 clock periods. This makes very efficient random access memory. The other system has 2×10^{12} words of virtual memory and 16 input/output ports with a total I/O rate of 3.2×10^9 bits per second. The arithmetic, logical and shift operations are handled in the pipes or functional units. There are up to 4 of these in one system and 12 in the other.

A "constant" in relation to these machines is that they are continuing to change or evolve into more powerful systems. For example, one new system will use a four-processor system to increase speed through multi-processing. Future systems will take advantage of liquid immersion technology to solve cooling problems. Semour Cray has announced successful tests of immersing a computer in a bath of clear inert liquid, a pure fluorocarbon.[11] The modules of this system will not have wires longer than 16 inches (41 cm). Also, the liquid becomes turbulent near heat, and this might be a maintenance tool for locating hot spots.

One of the most fascinating aspects of these computers is their relatively small size. Figure 5-1 shows a floor plan of a CDC-205. The unit is about 6 feet in height and does not require more than about 250 square feet of floor space. The Cray-1 (Figure 5-2) looks somewhat like a bench sofa, and likewise takes up little floor space, as shown. Both vendors are talking about smaller sizes for future models, on the order of one tenth the sizes illustrated in Figures 5-1 and 5-2. Instead of being the size of a bench, they will be the size of a desk. Despite the small size, these systems require several of the largest available scalar computers (front end machines) to feed them enough data to keep the processing stream going. The small size has largely to do with the short wire lengths required to get the phenomenal clock cycle times.

Computation Speeds

Computer capabilities are measured by the speed that instructions and mathematical operations can occur. A large scalar computer will operate at about 8 MIPS (million instructions per second). Vector computers will run at rates between 50 and 800 Mflps (megaflops or millions of floating point operations per

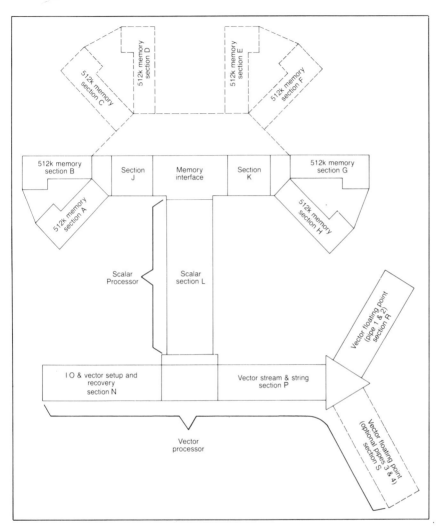

Figure 5-1. CDC's Cyber Model 205 vector computer system floor plan, as shown, takes up relatively little floor space, only about 250 square feet, in comparison to the work load it performs. (Courtesy Control Data Corp.)

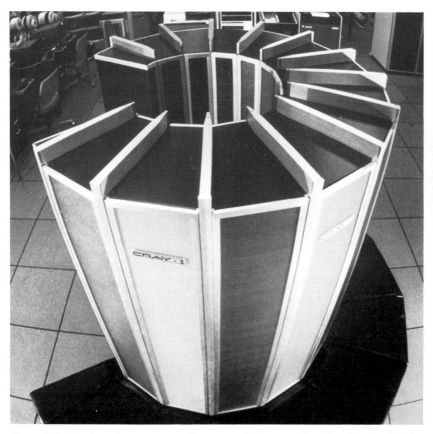

Figure 5-2. The Cray-1 vector processing system looks somewhat like a bench sofa. The small size of this, and other similar units, is due largely to the short wire length used to achieve short clock times.

second). A machine that does 800 Mflps has been designed, but has not yet been built. It will require 4 pipe lines, linked triads, and short precision (32-bit words) to accomplish this speed. (A linked triad is a special kind of vector operation of the form a scalar times a vector plus a vector.)

A single Mflp is equivalent to between 3 and 5 MIPS because floating point arithmetic has more complex instructions. This means that a vector processor manipulates between 25 and 400 times as much data as a large scalar computer. However, experience shows that the vector systems typically are running at 16 to 20 Mflps or 8 to 10 times the speed of a large serial system.[10]

A major determinant in specifying the processing rate is the clock period. The clock period is the time that passes between each processing step, once the pipes are full. Typical array processors attached to a VAX 11/780 minicomputer have a clock rate of 124 ns (nanoseconds). One ns is 10^{-9} seconds. A beam of light travels 30 cm in 1 ns. The available vector processors have clock rates of 9.5 ns, 12.5 ns,and 20ns, with projections of cycle times as low as 4.0 ns.

Software has to be completely rethought in order to take advantage of the extra speed of a vector processor. To illustrate this rethinking procedure, a programming procedure for sorting will be evaluated for a serial algorithm and a parallel algorithm. Probably everyone is acquainted with some form of sorting, whether it be in preparing to balance the check book, in alphabetizing a list of names, or in picking the seismic traces that fall within the migration aperture from a portion of the 3D data volume.

Serial sorting is illustrated using a bubble sort, a procedure whereby specified items appear to "bubble" to the top of a column or list. To start with there are 8 items in random order that are to be sorted, as shown in the left-hand column of Figure 5-3A. The bottom two items in the left-hand column are first compared. The larger number is placed on top of the smaller as illustrated in the second column. There are a total of 7 comparisons required to make the first pass.

A complete bubble sort of these 8 items takes 5 sequential passes as is illustrated in Figure 5-3B. The larger numbers appear to bubble to the top. There are 28 serial comparisons required to do this sort.[12]

Parallel sorting is described using an algorithm called the perfect shuffle. Figure 5-4A shows how the name was derived. The 8 items in the left-hand corner are to be sorted. They are first divided in half, and then interleaved in the same way a card deck is shuffled. Each of the 9 times the 8 items are shuffled they are passed through one of 3 comparators. These comparators pass the numbers, put the smaller number on top, or put the larger number on top as illustrated in Figure 5-4B. A perfect shuffle sorting of 8 items requires 36 comparisons of which 8 are redundant. However, if these comparisons can be performed simultaneously, then only 9 comparison clock periods are required for the perfect shuffle sort example. This further reduces to 7 clock periods when the 2 redundant comparisons are accounted for. The time to actually perform the perfect shuffle must also be considered. If this algor-

(text continued on page 122)

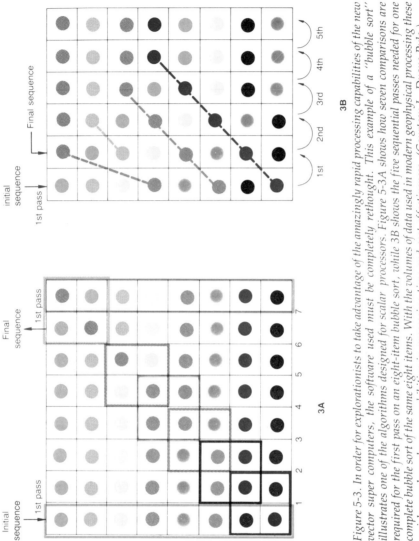

Figure 5-3. In order for explorationists to take advantage of the amazingly rapid processing capabilities of the new vector super computers, the software used must be completely rethought. This example of a "bubble sort" illustrates one of the algorithms designed for scalar processors. Figure 5-3A shows how seven comparisons are required for the first pass on an eight-item bubble sort, while 3B shows the five sequential passes needed for one complete bubble sort of the same eight items. With the volumes of data used in modern geophysical processing these serial procedures become prohibitive in processing time and cost effectiveness. (Courtesy L. Duane Pyle.)

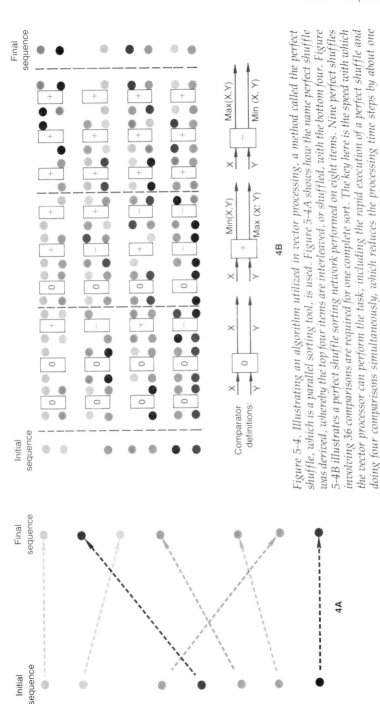

Figure 5-4. Illustrating an algorithm utilized in vector processing, a method called the perfect shuffle, which is a parallel sorting tool, is used. Figure 5-4A shows how the name perfect shuffle was derived, whereby the top four items are interleaved, or shuffled, with the bottom four. Figure 5-4B illustrates a perfect shuffle sorting network performed on eight items. Nine perfect shuffles involving 36 comparisons are required for one complete sort. The key here is the speed with which the vector processor can perform the task, including the rapid execution of a perfect shuffle and doing four comparisons simultaneously, which reduces the processing time steps by about one quarter, to about seven clock cycles. (Courtesy L. Duane Pyle.)

ithm is to work, it is important to be able to do the perfect shuffle fast, as is possible on a vector processor.[12]

These examples point out that it is not enough for explorationists and programmers to understand how to use vector processing capabilities. The algorithms must also be designed or redesigned for the vector computer environment. The data must be structured correctly so that data motion will take advantage of the vector processing capabilities.[13] At the computation rates being discussed, input and output can be critical to achieving cost effective processing.

Data motion, the rate at which data can be input into the computer, can be as important in using vector computers as the computation speed. An example of this is shown by some 1981-1983 research at the University of Houston's Research Computation Laboratory. The object is to extend a Fourier method wave equation modeling program[14] to three dimensions and vectorize it for use on the CDC-205 vector processor. The program utilizes five arrays of which three are calculated for each time step. Each of these arrays involves 16 million components requiring a total storage of 80 million words. However, only 2 million words can occupy the physical memory at any one time, and so the data is divided and stored on disc. Three of the arrays are accessed twice for each time step. Preliminary calculations indicate that the first pass is compute bound and the second pass is I/O bound.[15]

The I/O problems of today will seem small by the end of the decade. Both vendors are tying 6250-b.p.i. tape drives directly to I/O channels. One company claims to be able to read eight 6250-b.p.i. tapes simultaneously at full speed. However, this is not fast enough to handle problems faced today by seismic contracting companies. For example, Raymond C. Farrell of Seicom Delta United reports having problems with one 15-mile signbit seismic line with 2 million traces and 140 reels of tape. Under 1983 conditions, this processing sequence will typically take 200 ms/trace, or five 24-hour days to accomplish. This processing stream would include Vibroseis™ correlation, NMO (normal move out) correction, statics, mute, decon, and stack. Just properly mounting 140 reels of tape is a major job.

GEOPHYSICAL APPLICATION

Numerical reservoir modeling has been the single most important use of vector super computers in the petroleum industry to date. This application involves simulating the physical behavior of pressures, saturations, densities and similar quantities within the porous rocks and sands from which oil and gas are extracted. After the initial discovery well and the subsequent development wells delineate how large a field is, the reservoir engineer enters the picture. The very large numerical models are used to help decide how many more wells need to be drilled, where to drill them and how fast they can be produced. The numerical simulators solve simultaneously for three dependent variables at each of several hundred time steps for up to 12,000 nods.[16] This scale of number crunching can be approached in several areas of geophysical processing.

Three-dimensional seismic techniques provide the geophysical basis for using vector processors in seismic processing. Many of the 3D processing algorithms should be able to be vectorized and used cost effectively on a vector processor, especially processes like a full 3D migration that cannot realistically be accomplished on a standard scalar processor. There are several types of 3D migration for regularized (stacked) data: Kirchhoff summation, finite difference, Fourier transform, and direct inversion. Each procedure gives the same basic answer. However, vectorization of the different procedures will probably show more efficient processing of one of the methods than for another. It is possible that Kirchhoff summation techniques can be used to do a 3D migration of irregular data (prestack) using vector processing.[17]

Many of the more basic procedures can be vectorized for considerable processing time savings. The most basic processing procedures include filtering, deconvolution and correlation. Vibroseis™ correlation is an example of a processing procedure that probably can be done as a matrix multiply very rapidly on a vector processor. Again, velocity analysis is an ideal candidate for vectorization when working with 3D velocity analysis algorithms.

It is not unreasonable to project that the parallel logical operations associated with a vector processor will have great value in data base management, and possibly even interactive image processing and interpretation. The new display technologies are rapidly being tied to computers. As complex, large number crunching processing and numerical modeling techniques are vectorized, these display devices will provide an operator window to interactively work with and modify data sets.

One area where an explorationist might interact with a vector processor is forward modeling. Assuming some basic input/output problems can be solved, it is estimated that a 2D Fourier synthetic modeling program that takes up to ten hours to run on a VAX will take five minutes on a Cyber-205.[18] This same program took between 6 and 10 hours in a VAX 11/780 multiprocessing environment.[10] Once the data transfer and input/output problems are solved, it is reasonable to project that the vector processor will become an interactive interpretation aid.

It is also reasonable to speculate that as inversion and forward modeling techniques are improved there will be the development of computer interpretation procedures. The computer would interpret the raw data using pattern recognition procedures, and a forward modeling algorithm would be applied to the interpretation to make a seismic section. The result would be compared to the raw data, a new interpretation made based on the difference in the two sections and an iterative procedure followed until a satisfactory comparison is achieved. This is only a beginning in describing the potential of vector processors in geophysical processing and analysis.

SUMMARY

Geophysical processing has had a major impact on the development array processors, and will continue to have an effect as computer technology moves into the world of the vector super computers. The computation requirements necessary to correctly process a 3D seismic survey will be a major motivating force in these developments. These techniques bring reflection seismology into better conformance with reservoir engineering and similar computer fitting procedures will eventually be developed. There is still a lot of development that needs to occur, specifically in the process of software vectorization and data motion. However, there are many petroleum applications that appear to be ideal for this processing environment.

References

1. Nelson, H. R., Jr., "Trends in Multichannel Seismic Recording Systems," *World Oil*, pp. 135-142, Nov. 1981.
2. Nelson, H. R., Jr., "3D Seismic Techniques," *World Oil*, pp. 115-120, Dec. 1981.
3. Seismic Crew Survey, *The Leading Edge*, V. 1, No. 2, pp. 99-102, 1982.
4. French, W. S., "Two Dimensional and Three Dimensional Migration of Model Experiment Reflection Profiles," *Geophysics*, V. 39, No. 3, pp. 265-277, 1974.
5. Verm, R. W., University of Houston, Image Processing Laboratory, personal communications, 1981.
6. Technical Description CDC Cyber 200/Model 205, 36 pp., 1980.
7. Pyle, L. D., "A 3D Migration Program for the CDC CYBER 205," SAL Semi-Annual Progress Review, V. 7, pp. O1-O5, 1981.
8. Johnson, P. M., "An Introduction to Vector Processing," reprint *Computer Design*, 9 pp., February 1978.
9. Belzer, J. *et al.* "Convolution Array Processing," *Encylopedia of Computer Science and Technology*, Johnson, O. G., *et al*, Petroleum Industry section, V. 12, pp. 52-57, 1979.
10. Johnson, O. G., University of Houston, Computer Science Department, personal communication, 1981.
11. "Corporate Register," *Cray Channels*, V. 3, No. 2, pp. 12-14, 1981.
12. Pyle, L. D., University of Houston, Computer Science Department, personal communication, 1981.
13. Edwards, C. A. M., Control Data Corportion, Petroleum Technology Center, personal communication, 1981.
14. Kosloff, D. D., and E. Baysal, "Forward Modeling By a Fourier Method," SAL fourth year Semi-Annual Progress Review, V. 7, pp. H1-H22, 1981.
15. Johnson, O. G., Progress Report on the 3D Wave Equation Program for CDC CYBER 205, SAL fourth year Semi-Annual Progress Review, V. 7, pp. I1-I5.
16. Belzer, J. *et al*, "Numerical Reservoir Modeling," *Encylopedia of Computer Science and Technology*, Peaceman, D., *et al*, Petroleum Industry Section, V. 12, pp. 57-63, 1979.
17. Gardner, G. H. F., University of Houston, Allied Geophysical Laboratories, personal communications, 1981.
18. Kosloff, D. D., visiting professor of geophysics, University of Houston, personal communication, 1981.

CHAPTER 6

Numerical
and Physical Modeling

Physical and theoretical seismic modeling techniques are old and yet
new technologies. Traditionally these procedures have been used by
researchers as tools to better understand the relationship of the seismic
trace to the various geologic acoustic discontinuities that generate the
recorded response. This chapter briefly summarizes the historic development of modeling techniques, reviews a few current lessons being learned
from modeling, and shows how modeling can aid seismic interpreters.

Synthetic seismic trace generation has evolved into today's theoretical and physical modeling techniques. Synthetic seismic traces
are of interest to explorationists because the only material information about subsurface geology comes from sparsely spaced well
information in the form of cores or logs. From this one-dimensional
information the explorationist must correlate and interpret to
explain three-dimensional geologic structures and stratigraphic
sequences. Creating a synthetic seismic trace from a sonic log and
matching this to a seismic trace from a 2D or 3D seismic survey
enables the explorationist to expand available well information
along a line or over an area. In short, available data are extrapolated
into a probably three-dimensional, geologic setting. But how much
reliance can be placed on such extrapolation?

The information on each individual unprocessed seismic trace is
the acoustic response from three-dimensional subterranean geological surfaces. This is true whether the trace is from a check shot
survey, a seismic line or a seismic volume.[1] Even after the most
sophisticated processing algorithms have been applied and the

best possible interpretation made, these geologic surfaces are still "unknown." One way to gain confidence in the interpretation of these geologic sequences is to model them. Modeling techniques start with precisely known interfaces. If the information on the seismic traces derived from this known model interface is completely understood, there is more confidence in the interpretation of similar events from field generated data. Many different methods have been used to model these interfaces.

ONE-DIMENSIONAL MODELING

Most major oil company research groups used some form of physical modeling before digital computers provided simpler testing. Frank Levin, now at Exxon Production Research, was doing 1D (one-dimensional) physical model experiments as early as 1949.[2] These experiments consisted of measuring the air wave that traveled through long thin tubes with changing diameters. In this type of a model, the cross-sectional area is proportional to the density, and the "springiness" to density times velocity. An impulse was generated by a magnet on a propeller that passed an induction coil. The signal was displayed on an analog oscilloscope.

Synthetic seismic traces from well logs are the most common example of 1D theoretical modeling. An example of early 1D modeling that predates active use of digital computers is the Seismoline. This device, built by John Sherwood at Chevron, models the wave equation solution with an electric circuit. The seismic response in this unit is generated by an electric delay line. In this circuit, an inductance series is proportional to mass while a variable capacitor is shunted across the line to calibrate the velocity. The scaled velocities on this modeling device can range from 5,000 to 22,000 fps. The bed thicknesses are kept constant, while velocities can vary. An impulsive electrical source can be set off anywhere in depth. The output of the circuit is monitored by an analog oscilloscope.[3] The response can thus be evaluated in real time. Back in the early 1960s every division in Chevron had one of these units, because they were more convenient than using digital computers.

TWO-DIMENSIONAL MODELING

One of the first publications on physical modeling was the work of Oliver, Press and Ewing in 1954.[4] This experiment studies 2D (two-dimensional) seismology problems using ultrasonic pulses propagating in small scale models. Thin discs (1/16 in. thick and 20 in. in diameter) were used as a medium for studying surface waves propagating around the circumference of the disc. By building the disc from concentric rings of various materials, more complex models were generated. The source pulses were initiated at one position on the edge of the disc and then measured at some other position on the edge.

Southern Methodist University has a 2D modeling system that was built and used at Mobil Field Research for many years. This modeling system used thin sheets of various metals with various thicknesses to simulate vertical 2D cross sections. A 2D faulted horizon is represented by connecting two different sheets of metal with a matching step. Piezoelectric transducers are used as the source and receiver. These transducers are placed at specific positions along the top of the cross section where a seismic trace is desired, and then moved along the cross section to generate a seismic section.

Similar physical modeling research was done by most major oil companies. The author is aware that there also has been extensive work at Amoco, Exxon, Gulf, Texaco, and by Russian geophysicists. Other variations of 2D modeling systems included milling the metal cross section sheets to different thicknesses at interface boundaries, drilling small holes in the sheets to vary the velocity, and attaching plastic sheets or other materials to change the thickness of the thin cross sections. An important factor in this work is that the wave length be long compared to the thickness of the cross sections. These techniques are not used widely today, but they are good for illustration purposes.

Another related physical model experiment was carried out by John Woods, and presented as an SEG Distinguished Lecture in 1967. In this study, spark plugs were used as the seismic source. The air waves that were generated were 3D, but they were reflected off single layer 2D structures. The horizons that were evaluated were built out of plywood. The first experiment was to measure the response for various source-receiver positions across an edge simulating a fault. The next step was to evaluate the response from discs of different sizes. The seismic response from a source-receiver combination directly above the center of a disc consists of a specular reflection from the surface and a diffraction, the sum of energy reflected from the disc perimeter, arriving a short time later. The size of the disc determines the delay in the arrival of the diffraction energy. This can be related directly to the tuning thickness of thin beds. In Woods' work the disc that had a two-wavelength delay between the specular reflection and the perimeter edge diffraction was replaced with rings with the same outer diameter. The diameter of the ring hole was varied. This work shows that seismic energy comes from a large area and not from a "reflection point" or a "fault line."[5]

Other models that were evaluated included 2D anticlines and synclines. These were 2D in the sense that the models varied in elevation only along the cross section axis. The depth along the strike axis was constant. Extensive spark-gap modeling studies also were carried out by Shell.[6]

Physical modeling became much less common with the development of digital computers. Programs were written to give the expected seismic response for a specific set of acoustic discontinuities. Ray tracing programs have been used for the last 10 years on storage tube computer terminals to help interpreters visualize where recorded energy is coming from. This has been very helpful in defining what portions of complex 2D structures are expected to be seen on the seismic section. However, these techniques are being used less as theoretical modeling techniques become more sophisticated.

Kirchhoff forward modeling is one widely used method of making 2D and also single layer 3D theoretical models. This theory is based on the theoretical diffraction response shown in Figure 6-1.[7] Note that the synthetic seismic profile across the fault edge is composed of two parts, a reflection and a diffraction. A normal incidence reflection from the boundary occurs up to the edge, and a positive diffraction event with the same polarity occurs beyond the termination of the reflector. However, there is a negative diffraction event on the side of the edge with the reflecting boundary. These diffraction events have opposite polarity (they are 180° out of phase) and represent the dipole nature of this type of modeling.[8]

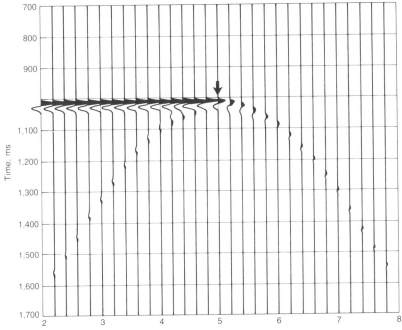

Figure 6-1. Wide-band seismic response from a flat boundary. Note that the response amplitude drops by half at the edge. Also, the diffraction has the same polarity beyond the reflector, but is 180° out of phase on the same side as the reflecting boundary. (After A.W. Trorey.[7])

In Kirchhoff forward modeling, the boundary is mathematically defined as a 2D strip that goes into and out of the plane described by the cross section in Figure 6-1. The boundary is made very short into a strip. Then a series of these strips are put together to define faults, synclines, anticlines and other structures that can be related to subsurface geology. The synthetic seismic response for a single trace turns out to be the summation of the diffractions from these mathematical strips for a specific source-receiver position. By repeating the procedure for different source-receiver positions, synthetic seismic sections are created.

The finite difference method of modeling extends this single layer approach to multiple 2D layers. Each layer can be assigned a different density-velocity combination in order to represent the reflection coefficients or the acoustic impedance expected from different geologic interfaces. This method of forward modeling has been presented in the literature by Amoco researchers.[9,10] The seismic modeling algorithms that use finite differences operate on a dis-

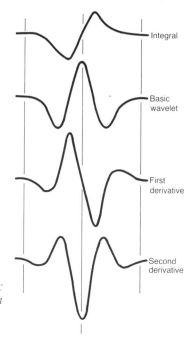

Figure 6-2. A graphical representation of a basic wavelet and its integral and derivative shapes in the time domain. (Courtesy F. J. Hilterman .[8])

crete mesh. This mesh is filled with the elastic constants that describe the geologic model, including density and velocity. The pressure response is then calculated for each time step to create synthetic traces.

Each of the forward modeling methods requires that a derivative of the waveform be calculated as part of the algorithm. Figure 6-2 gives a graphical summary of a wavelet, the integral and derivative shapes in the time domain. With finite difference modeling there needs to be about 10 samples per wavelength in order to approximate the derivative of the waveform.[9] This is a critical factor in attempting to expand this forward modeling technique to three dimensions.

Overall, the finite difference approach is simple and may be implemented readily. This method of forward modeling provides proper relative amplitudes for the varous seismic wave arrivals. Contributions from converted waves, Rayleigh wave, diffractions from faulted zones and head waves are all included in the seismic response.

One of the advantages of this type of theoretical modeling procedure is that the wave from can be stopped in time. This allows a "snapshot" of the position of the wave front for any specified time to be plotted. Kelly, *et al*, described this capability for finite difference modeling.[10] This capability is useful in evaluating where energy is coming from for different geologic models.

When these "snapshots" are animated, the interpreter is given a tool that allows him to watch the various seismic waves move through a model. By displaying "snapshot" movies both forward and backward, events that cannot otherwise be interpreted can be followed from the time they were recorded back to the time when they were generated. This is shown in the sequence of wavefront "snapshots" in Figure 6-3 taken from an animation of work by Dan Kosloff and Edip Baysal at the University of Houston's Seismic Acoustics Laboratory (SAL).[11] The movie brings the wave fronts "alive," and complex wave interactions are easy to visually separate.

The training and interpretational usefulness of this technique is obvious when a movie of a sequence of snapshots is seen. The 2D wedge physical model experiment at the SAL had an unidentified "mystery event" (labeled "E" on Figure 6-4A). It turns out that this is a diffraction from the top of the wedge. Both the physical model and a physical model seismic section are shown in Figure 6-4. This sequence of snapshots were generated using the Fourier method.

Fourier forward modeling by Dan Kosloff is a hybrid technique that calculates the derivatives in the frequency domain. The major benefit here is that only two samples per wavelength are needed in order to approximate the derivative of the waveform.[11] This is a savings of a factor of five in the number of samples required to define a 1D forward model. This savings factor expands to 25 for a 2D model and 125 for a 3D forward model. This becomes a significant factor in determining whether multi-layered, multi-velocity 3D models can be run using a realistic amount of computer time.

THREE-DIMENSIONAL MODELING

Frank Levin also was involved in some of the early 3D physical modeling studies. In one project, a two-bed model consisted of 3 in. of cement over a 1-in. sheet of marble. Ultrasonic pulse

(text continued on page 136)

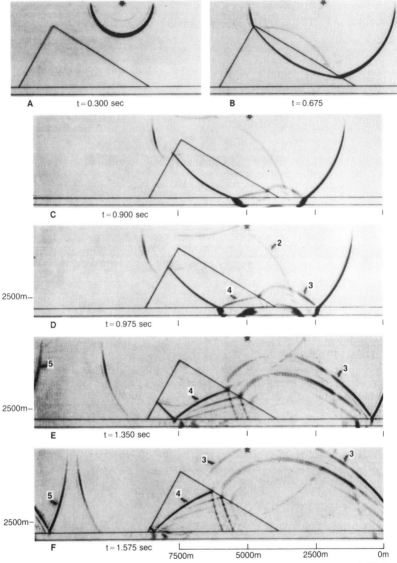

A   t = 0.300 sec   B   t = 0.675

C   t = 0.900 sec

2500m—

D   t = 0.975 sec

2500m—

E   t = 1.350 sec

2500m—

F   t = 1.575 sec
        7500m   5000m   2500m   0m

Figure 6-3. A sequence of wavefront "snapshots" calculated using the Kosloff, Baysal Fourier modeling technique. The pressure response is calculated at specific time steps and then the snapshots are "animated" to help interpret specific events. Event 2 is reflected energy off of the low-velocity wedge. Events 3 and 4 are reflected energy off of the high-velocity flat base. Event 5 is wrap-around due to the Fourier transforms used in this method. (After Kosloff and Baysal.)

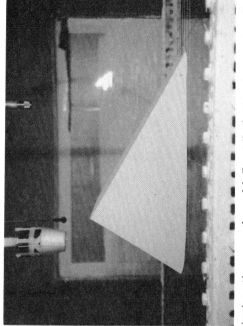

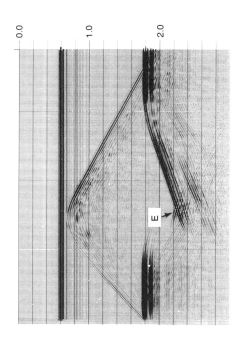

Figure 6-4. A 2D wedge physical model is shown accompanied by a seismic section across the model. Event E, the "mystery event on the physical model section, is the diffraction energy from the top of the wedge.

generators were used as the source.[12] Although the model was really 2D, in that it did not vary along one spatial axis, there were some interesting results. One conclusion (taken for granted today) was that two in-line detectors could reduce surface waves.

The biggest problem with the physical model approach is that once the models are built it is necessary to start over from the beginning to change the model. However, this is not a problem if critical 2D strike and dip sections are generated theoretically to make sure the problem to be solved is being properly addressed.

Numerical Modeling

One widely used 3D numerical modeling technique is Kirchhoff forward modeling. For example, the Geoquest AIMS modeling package is based on this method. The 3D Kirchhoff technique uses triangular plates to represent a 3D surface. In the same way that the diffraction responses from small strips were added to give the reflection response for the 2D case, the 3D method adds the diffraction responses from the triangular plates to derive the expected seismic response.[13] The source and receiver can be arbitrarily placed in 3D space above the defined surface. This allows for the synthetic generation of single traces, multifold lines, or seismic volumes. The literature only describes this type of modeling for single surfaces. However, Hilterman[8] has developed a multilayered version of this algorithm.

A vectorized Fourier method of forward modeling is presently (1983) being improved and expanded for 2D and 3D cases at the University of Houston's Research Computation Laboratory (RLC).[14] It is now possible to generate synthetic seismic traces over any arbitrary multilayered, multi-velocity 3D model on a Cyber-205 using these programs. It is also possible to generate 3D "snapshot" sequences that can be animated on a true 3D display device. It is not feasible to do this with finite difference modeling because the number of samples required makes storage and computation time requirements unrealistic, even on a vector processor.

There are many interpretative lessons that can be learned using the 3D forward modeling techniques. Fred Hilterman[13] and Luh-Cheng Liang[15] have presented illustrations of these lessons. Synthetic sections taken across a geologic basin are good examples of their work.[16] Three theoretical models are illustrated in Figure 6-5: a triangular representation of a symmetrical basin, an isometic drawing of an oblong basin and the location of eight synthetic sections overlain on a 100-ft contour map of the oblong basin. The scaled radii of curvature in the two principal planes of this oblong basin are 4,000 and 7,000 ft, respectively. The scaled velocity down to the modeled interface is 12,000 fps. The basin is 750 ft deep and the square edge of the isometric drawing scales to 12,000 ft on a side. Figure 6-6 depicts the raw sections generated for a source-receiver placed 5,500 ft above the model. One 3D effect is shown on Line 4. Here, focused events from the far flank of the structure are not connected to the upper horizon. Figure 6-7 reveals 2D migrations of the sections in Figure 6-6. Note that there appears to be a fault on Line 6 and a graben on Lines 5 and 7. Much of the ringiness on the migrated sections is due to spurious events from out-of-plane lip of the basin.

It is important to note that each of the theoretical modeling methods is forced to assume the characteristics of seismic noise. In many cases, diffractions, multiples and thin bed "noise" of the real world *cannot* be represented as well by numerical modeling as by physical modeling.

Physical Modeling

A 3D physical modeling box using the spark gap method was described by Fred Hilterman in 1970.[17] Later Bill French designed and built a 1-cubic-meter water tank that has proved more effective for 3D physical modeling. This was built for Gulf Research and Development in Pittsburgh. A paper in 1974 describes how the system was used to collect data over 3D models. These data were used to study 2D and 3D migration techniques.[18]

A more recent example of work done with this system is an article by John McDonald, *et al,* in 1981.[19] This work describes how the water tank physical modeling system was used to solve an interpretation problem in an area without appreciable structure in the subsurface. A volume of physical model data was processed to produce an instantaneous phase horizontal section. These sections were compared to similarly processed field data to show that areal seismic methods can be used to determine the extent of an acoustic

(text continued on page 141)

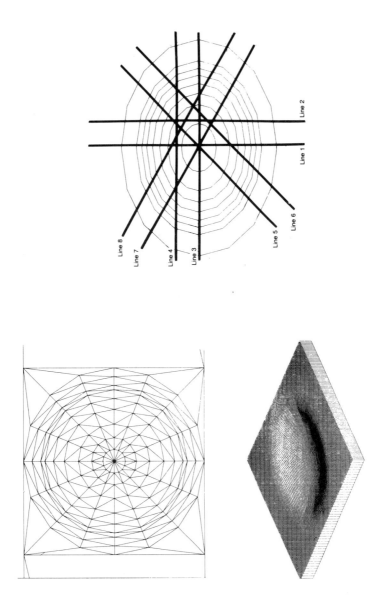

Figure 6-5. The definition of a theoretical basin for Kirchhoff forward modeling is illustrated here. A map view of the triangular plates for a symmetrical basin is shown, followed by an isometric view of the oblong basin and a location map for specific synthetic sections called Lines 1-8. (After Liang and Hilterman.[16])

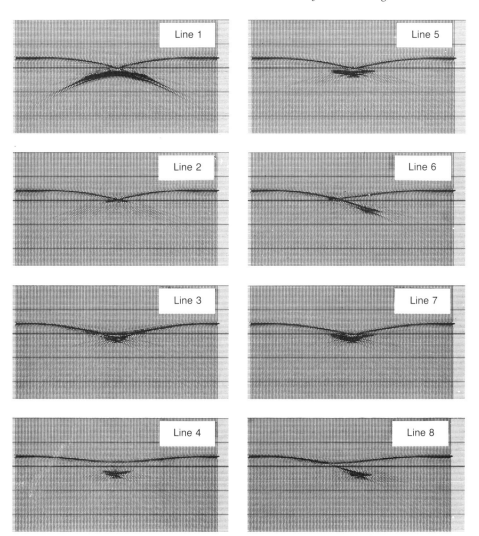

Figure 6-6. Unprocessed or raw sections generated across the oblong basin model of Figure 6-5 show the complex seismic events generated by a simple model. Note the expected bow-tie effect on Line 1. Line 4 shows a 3D effect where focused energy from the far flanks of the structure are not connected to the reflected horizon. (After Liang and Hilterman.[16])

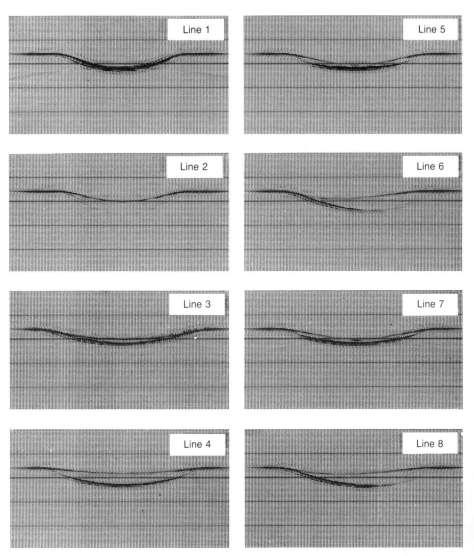

Figure 6-7. Migrated data from the model in Figure 6-5 illustrates that 2D migration does not properly image 3D structures. Note the apparent graben on Lines 5 and 7, and the apparent, large fault on Line 6. (After Liang and Hilterman.[16])

discontinuity caused by a pinnacle reef. (Figure 7-2 is a computer graphics display of a physical model used in this study.)

This type of water tank physical modeling system has been expanded at the SAL. The SAL model tank is 8 ft by 6 ft by 5 ft deep. Everything is scaled. Standard scale parameters are 1 in. equals 1,000 ft, 150 kHz equals 30 Hz, and the 0.2 microsecond sample rate equals 1 millisecond (ms). Models of the subsurface structures are made out of plexiglass (scaled velocity 21,600 fps) or different silicon rubbers (scaled velocity around 8,000 fps). The models are normally smaller than 24 in. by 24 in. by 5 in. (scaled 4 mi by 4 mi by 1 mi deep).

Physical models have been made to represent various structural and stratigraphic sequences.[16,20] There have been several proprietary models built for individual SAL sponsors that represent specific exploration problems or fields being developed. A very complex model was completed in 1982 as a proprietary project. The model is 32 in. by 30 in. by 17 in. (scaled 6 mi by 5.7 mi by 3.2 mi deep or 9.8 km by 9.1 km by 5.2 km deep). This model has seven independently contoured and faulted horizons and weighs about 800 lbs. (360 kgms).

Some of these multi-layered models have been built directly from an interpreter's contour maps. Figure 6-8 shows a simple example of one of the contour maps that was converted to the two-layer, faulted anticline physical model named SALFAN[21] This model was built by cutting the contours out of clay. The wedges between contours were then filled in with clay, and a plaster negative cast was made. The bottom layer of silicon rubber was poured into this cast from the bottom. The upper layer of this model was poured from a side, between the bottom layer and the second cast. The resulting physical model is a 3D representation of the two contour maps. This model is 16 in. square, or about 3 mi (5 km) on a side scaled.

These models are placed on a wire mesh in the center of the water tank, and then data are collected over the models in a manner similar to data collection in the field. The source and receiver are high frequency piezoelectric transducers that are moved above the surface of the model by a pair of plotters. Standard patterns of data collection can be set up to simulate any kind of field procedures. In fact, the physical modeling tank can be used to collect data that are

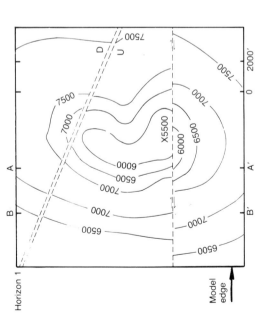

Figure 6-8. The contour map shown is first converted to clay contours to make a physical model. The wedges between contours are then filled in with clay. A plaster negative cast is made, and the silicon rubber, or other model material, is poured into this cast. The physical model shown is called SALFAN.[21]

difficult or impossible to obtain in the field, like tape sequential CMP gathers. The plotters move under computer control to the nearest 10 ft in the x and y axes and to the nearest foot in the z axes. The data are recorded in tape sequential format on standard magnetic tapes.

It takes an average of 1.5 sec for the plotters to move to the next shot point position, to fire the transducers and to record the data on tape. The plotters can be moved according to a preset pattern, or by having each source-receiver position specified on cards or magnetic tape. A 24-fold line, 5 mi (8 km) long and with a 330-ft (100-m) trace spacing will take less than 2 hours to collect. A 3D T-spread survey with 48 receivers, 96 shots per receiver setup, and 12 setups, will take about 24 hours to collect. Once the model is properly located and the data collection started, the system can be left to run itself for up to 16,000 traces, or about 7 hours, with automatic switching to new tape drives.

Simple models have proved to generate data sets that require detailed evaluation to understand all of the events. Therefore, it is useful to do a theoretical model study before designing and building the physical model. It is easier to build the model right the first time than to modify it by adding and removing material on exposed surfaces. However, when compared to the cost of a well drilled in the wrong place, building a new model that answers an exploration problem is very cost effective.

Figure 6-9 is an example of a simple model, called SALFRS, that can be used in many ways to help interpreters understand some common exploration problems. This model is a series of plexiglass cylinders sitting on a flat base plate.[22] Figure 6-9 shows two single-fold sections across this model. Note the difference in the reflection as the discs get smaller. Assume the exploration objective, say a reef or a sand lens, were the size of one of these Fresnel discs. Note the response from that size disc on Line 10 where the line passes 2,000 ft (0.6 km) from the center of the objective.

Another simple physical model example is the multi-velocity structural model SALHCI.[23] The model is shown in the water tank in Figure 6-10. This geologic model is an asymmetrical, double plunging anticline with scaled relief of 1,750 ft. (0.5 km). The upper 750 ft (225 m) is a low velocity (8,000 fps or 2,400 mps) cap made of silicon rubber. The lower portion of the dome represents a high velocity layer (21,600 fps or 6,600 mps) and is made of plexiglass.

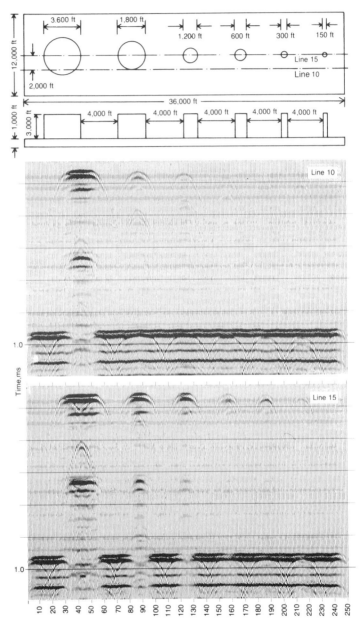

Figure 6-9. A map view (including section locations) and side view of physical model SALFRS is shown. Note the expected response on the seismic section for Line 15 as the cylinders get smaller. The 2,000-ft separation between the sections shows the importance of proper spatial sampling in order to see events that can indicate significant hydrocarbon prospects.[22]

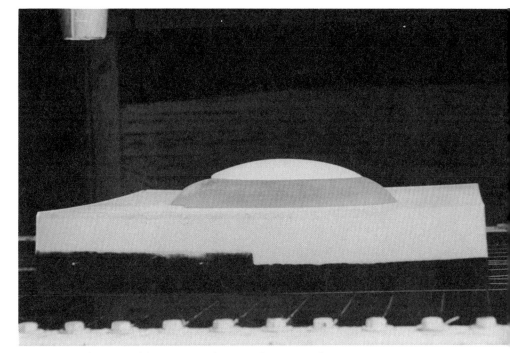

Figure 6-10. The 3D model SALHCI is shown in the water tank.

The surrounding water velocity scales to 11,633 fps (3,545 mps). Figure 6-11 shows an example map for one set of data consisting of 37 lines of single-fold common-offset data. Accompanying are examples of two sections of raw data. Note the sideswipe energy coming in when the line passes about one-half mile from the structure on Line 5. Line 20 is across the center of the model. It shows the velocity push-down due to the low velocity (gas) cap and the velocity pull-up of the plexiglass base on the flanks of the dome. These graphic examples can be very useful in training interpreters to find drillable structures on their field seismic sections.

Complex models generate data that is especially useful for training explorationists. There are also many results that need further research and detailed evaluation. Areas that have received some evaluation using complex models include acquisition studies; the effect of offset or depth on the seismic wavelet; minimum required sampling in time and space to evaluate specific geological sequences with seismic techniques; tuning effects of thin beds; the

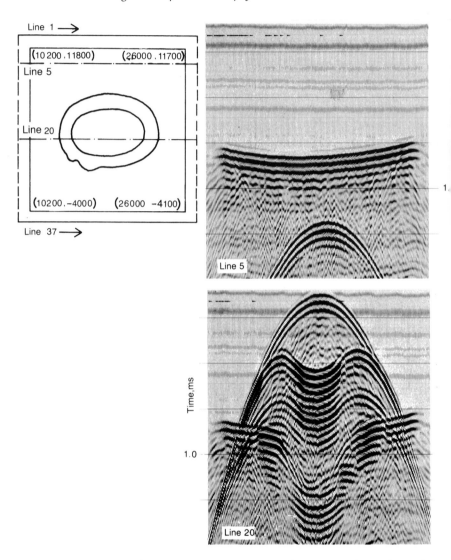

Figure 6-11. A map view of the SALHCI model is shown with two seismic lines referenced. Seismic sections for each of the lines are illustrated. Note the sideswipe from the model edge as indicated in the section for Line 5. The velocity push-down from the low velocity (gas) cap is shown in the section from Line 20.[23]

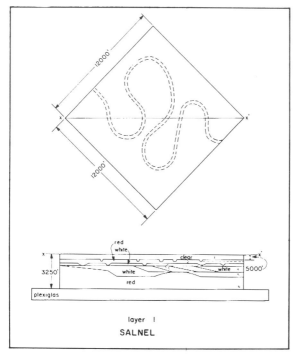

Figure 6-12A. Line drawing of SALNEL showing the six different layers represented by the model.[25]

accuracy of processing algorithms in correcting a raw data set; the usefulness of horizontal time-slice sections in interpreting 3D data volumes; the importance of using vertical and horizontal sections to generate an accurate interpretation; etc. Two complex SAL models that have been released will be used to illustrate some of the applications of complex 3D physical models.

The first model represents a Gulf Coast sedimentary sequence of six layers and is named SALNEL.[24] The top layer is flat. The second layer has a meandering stream channel, with a third layer underneath representing braided stream channels. Layers 4 and 5 consist of four parallel dipping reflectors representing a progressive beach front. Layer 6 at the base is the SALGLF model (Chapter 4, Figure 6). Figure 6-12A is a line drawing representation of the model. Note

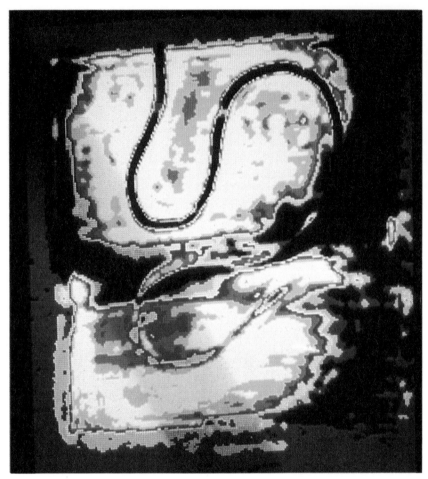

Figure 6-12B. Time-slice or horizontal section through the SALNEL meandering stream.

in Figures 6-12B and 12C how well time-slices through the 3D migrated data volume define the meandering stream and braided streams of layers 2 and 3. Figure 6-12D shows an interpretation of four of the horizons from one view. Note the apparent fault across the top three layers. This is due to the platform settling a little during the 3D data acquisition. This problem with the platform was later solved. Figure 6-12E shows an Adage display close-up on a cross-section through the channels. The interpretation of this data defined the large braided channels to have a maximum width of 480

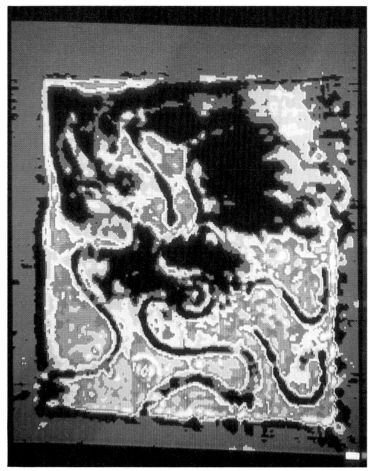

Figure 6-12C. Time-slice or horizontal section through the SALNEL braided streams.

ft (146 m). Although the channel width had been cataloged at 750 ft (229 m), when the plaster cast was measured, the maximum scaled channel width at this layer was 470 ft (143 m).[25]

A more complex geologic structural problem is illustrated by the North Sea model SALNOR.[26] This model was built as a proprietary project for Statoil and later released to the SAL consortium. SALNOR is a generalization of a typical North Sea geologic sequence, with reflectors to represent the Top Paleocene, Top Cretaceous, J-Unconformity, Top and Base Brent sandstone, and the Top

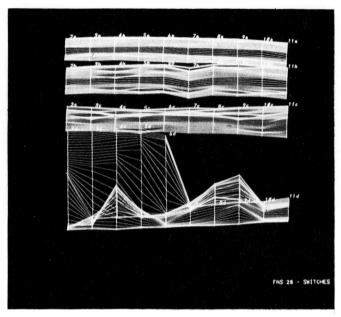

Figure 6-12D. A surface fit across the interpretation of four SALNEL horizons from one view.

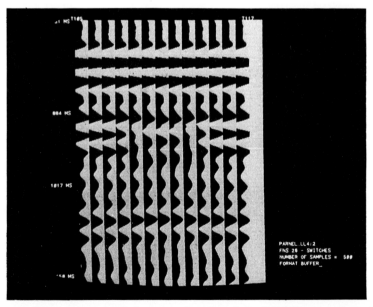

Figure 6-12E. A close-up vertical cross-section through the SALNEL channels displayed on the Adage RSG. The channel width can be very accurately measured from this data, but the depth measurement has some problems because of the source wavelet.

Figure 6-13A. The completed SALNOR physical model in the modeling tank.

and Base Statfjord sandstone. Figure 6-13A shows the completed physical model in the modeling tank.

Figure 6-13B is the plaster cast for the *Base Statfjord* horizon, and Figure 6-13C shows the rubber model of this layer. Figures 6-13D and E illustrate seismic sections as defined by the location map (Figure 6-13F). One real value of this model has come in mixing horizontal and vertical seismic sections to teach interactive interpretation techniques. Figures 6-13G and H are selected horizontal sections that illustrate the type of visual information available from 3D surveys.[27] After the data were collected the model was cut into 16 blocks for illustrative purposes. These blocks are tremendous teaching aids for someone working on interpreting a portion of the 3D data volume. Animated sequences through this model very closely parallel field data displayed in the same way.

SUMMARY

Physical and numerical modeling have been used throughout the history of seismic exploration as a tool to understand field-

(text continued on page 155)

Figure 6-13B. A view of the SALNOR J-Unconformity plaster cast after it was shaved off to the Base Statfjord horizon.

Figure 6-13C. The silicon rubber for deeper layers was added by pouring between the model and the plaster cast. This shows the SALNOR model after the Statfjord horizon had been poured.

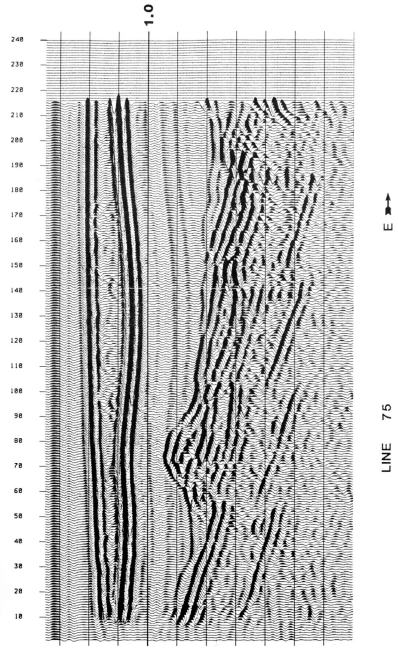

Figure 6–13D. An east-west vertical seismic section across the SALNOR model. The top three horizons represent the Top Paleocene, Top Cretaceous, and J-Unconformity. The other horizon easily recognized, which has four faults, is the Base Statfjord horizon.

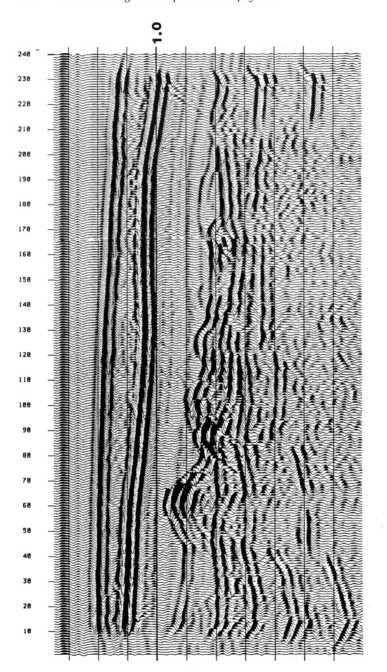

Figure 6–13E. A north-south vertical seismic section across the SALNOR model. The same horizons noted in Figure 6–13D can be recognized. On the left side, the Top and Base Brent and Top and Base Statfjord are also easily seen.

N ↑

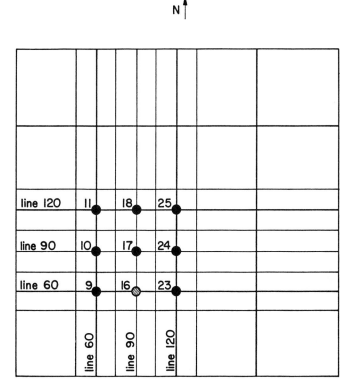

● Producing Well
● Available Drill Sites
☐ Lease Block 10

Figure 6–13F. A map showing the relationship of 7 north-south, 7 east-west, and 9 possible drilling locations. This is part of an interpretation training exercise.

recorded data. As time has passed, these tools have been improved. The modeling techniques described are finding their way out of the research labs and into use by explorationists. It is very helpful for a person developing new algorithms to have a set of data from a known feature on which to test the new programs. Seismic interpreters can use these tools to come to a better understanding of their seismic sections and to explain complex events on field data. As 3D modeling techniques are improved, case histories will be developed that document how field development has been aided by physical and numerical modeling.

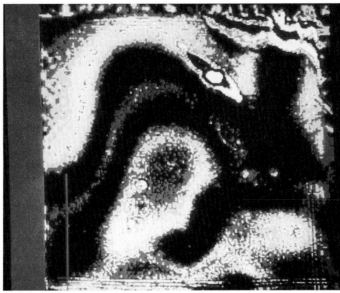

Figure 6–13G. A horizontal seismic section from a 3D survey collected across the North Sea physical model. The time-slice section is at 1.06 seconds and cuts the J-Unconformity structural highs.

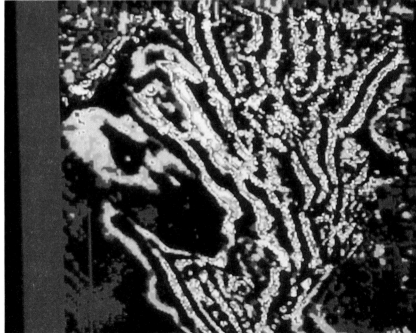

Figure 6–13H. A time-slice section from the same SALNOR 3D survey at time 1.22 seconds. At this depth the section cuts through the two dipping, producing Brent and Statfjord sandstones. The fault cuts are easily identified, especially when a sequence of time-slices are animated like a movie.

References

1. Nelson, H. R., Jr. "3D Seismic Tehniques Aid Exploration Development," *World Oil*, pp. 115-120, December, 1981.
2. Levin, F. K., Exxon Production Research, personal communication, 1981.
3. Sherwood, J. W. C., "The Seismoline, An Analog Computer of Theoretical Seismograms," *Geophysics*, V. 27, No. 1, pp. 19-34, 1962.
4. Oliver, J., Press, F., and Ewing, M., "Two-Dimensional Model Seismology," *Geophysics*, V. 19, No. 2, pp. 202-219, 1954.
5. Woods, J. P., "A Seismic Model Using Sound Waves in Air," *Geophysics*, V. 40, No. 4, pp. 593-607, 1975.
6. Sherwood, J. W. C., Geophysical Development Corporation, personal communication, 1981.
7. Trorey, A. W., "A Simple Theory for Seismic Diffractions, *Geophysics*, V. 35, No. 5, pp. 762-784, 1970.
8. Hilterman, F. J., Geophysical Development Corporation, personal communication, 1981.
9. Alford, R. M., Kelly, K. R., and Boore, D. M., "Accuracy of Finite-Difference Modeling of the Acoustic Wave Equation," *Geophysics*, V. 39, No. 6, pp. 834-842, 1974.
10. Kelly, K. R., *et al*, "Synthetic Seismograms: A Finite-Difference Approach," *Geophysics*, V. 41, No. 1, pp. 2-27, 1976.
11. Kosloff, D. D., and Baysal, E., "Forward Modeling by a Fourier Method," presentation at 51st annual international SEG meeting, Los Angeles, 1981 (see abstract, *Geophysics*, V. 47, No. 4, pp. 460-461, 1982).
12. Levin, F. K., and Hibard, H. D., "Three-Dimensional Seismic Model Studies," *Geophysics*, V. 20, No. 1, pp. 19-32, 1955.
13. Hilterman, F. J. "Interpretative Lessons from Three-Dimensional Modeling," preprint of presentation given at 46th annual international SEG meeting, Houston, Texas, 1976 (see also abstract, *Geophysics*, V. 42, No. 1, p. 156, 1977).
14. Nelson, H. R., Jr., "New vector super computers promote seismic advancements," *World Oil*, pp. 155-160, January 1982.
15. Liang, L. C., and Hilterman, F. J., "2D Seismic Migration Effects from 3D Geological Structures," Offshore Technology Conference Proceedings, paper No. 4096, pp. 263-269, 1981.
16. Liang, L. C., and Hilterman, F. J. "2D Effects from 3D Structures," SAL Semi-Annual Progress Review, V. 7, pp. L1-74, 1981.
17. Hilterman, F. J., "Three-Dimensional Seismic Modeling," *Geophysics*, V. 35, No. 6, pp. 1,020-1,037, 1970.
18. French, W. S., "Two Dimensional and Three-Dimensional Migration of Model Experiment Reflection Profiles," *Geophysics*, V. 39, No. 3, pp. 265-277, 1974.
19. McDonald, J. A., Gardner, G. H. F., and Kotcher, J. S., "Areal Seismic Methods for Determining the Extent of Acoustic Discontinuities," *Geophysics*, V. 46, No. 1, pp. 2-16, 1981.
20. Hilterman, F. J., Nelson, H. R. Jr., Gardner, G. H. F., "Physical Modeling: An Aid for Production Geophysicists," Offshore Technology Conference Proceedings, paper No. 4022, pp. 139-147, 1981.

21. SALFAN Physical Model Catalog, No. 4, SAL Semi-Annual Progress Review, V. 7, pp. J46-52, 1981.
22. SALFRS Physical Model Catalog, No. 4, SAL Semi-Annual Progress Review, V. 7, pp. J 33-37, 1981.
23. SALCHI, SAL Physical Model Catalog No. 2, pp. 91-99, 1980.
24. SALCHI SAL Physical Model Catalog No. 5, SAL Annual Progress Review, V. 8, p. 113-125, 1981.
25. Fisher, D. A., Nelson, H. R., Jr., and Verm, R. W., "Interactive Display and Interpretation of a Complex Physical Model After 3D Migration," SAL Semi-Annual Progress Review, V. 9, pp. 423-448, 1982.
26. SALNOR, SAL Physical Model Catalog No. 6, SAL Semi-Annual Progress Review, V. 9, pp. 43-71, 1982.
27. Nelson, H. R., Jr., *et al*, "SALNOR-North Sea Model: Building, Data Acquisition and Interpretation," SAL Semi-Annual Progress Review, V. 9, pp. 321-360, 1982.

CHAPTER 7

Interactive Computer Graphics

New advances in computer graphics technology are cautiously being accepted in today's world of exploration geophysics. There have been tremendous advances in CAD/CAM (computer aided design/computer aided manufacturing), aerospace, medical and other industries that are now being evaluated for their potential use in displaying and keeping track of the large quantities of seismic data being collected,[1] processed[2] and interpreted today. This chapter describes recent advances in display equipment and summarizes the expected impact on exploration geophysics.

Data volumes from a 3D seismic survey[3] require new methods of storage, manipulation and display. With the increased use of high-density tapes, large capacity disc drives and solid-state memory chips, the problem of enough data storage for interactive geophysical analysis has been effectively solved. However, few, if any, companies have established a workable system for either seismic data base management or interactive seismic display.

Part of the reason for the current limited use of interactive displays is that the end product of data collection and processing is still paper sections. As the amount of data to be evaluated increases, the amount of paper used increases even faster. When management makes a strong commitment to utilizing available computer display technology, it will be required that efficient procedures for retrieving data from the seismic storage medium for display on a graphics terminal be developed.

TRADITIONAL DISPLAY TERMINALS

In the past, when an exploration geophysicist talked of computer graphics, he usually referred to a Tektronix (note disclaimer in preface) storage tube display terminal. This terminal typically has a 19-in. diagonal screen with both refresh and storage display capabilities. The resolution can range from 1,024 by 780 to 4,096 by 3,120 displayable raster points. A typical system will have on the order of 2,048 by 1,536 displayable points.[4] This means that the screen is displaying 153 dots per inch along the x-axis and 115 dots per inch along the y-axis. The resolution on a standard 8 1/2-inch-wide Gould plotter is 80 dots per inch. Even though storage tube resolution is greater than this, the screen limits the amount of data that can be displayed along both the x and y axes. A plotter allows long strips of data to be printed out and spliced if desired, so that a large scale display of an entire seismic line can be viewed as a whole by a geophysical interpreter. Also, electrostatic plotters are up to 22 in. wide and have resolution of up to 200 dots per inch.

Because of the small screen size, the amount of data that can be viewed is reduced; as a result, the major applications of computer graphics display technology have been in modeling rather than production work. There are examples of complex ray-tracing algorithms in the libraries of most of the major exploration companies. Other common programs have included gravity and magnetics modeling, synthetic trace generation (especially to evaluate potential bright spots, or direct hydrocarbon indicators) and contouring packages. These terminals can be connected to a hardcopy unit, so that a paper record of the progress of each session can be kept.

In addition, many of these systems are augmented with local intelligence and peripherals to reduce the mainframe computer processing requirements needed to support remote terminals. Plug-in firmware, a local software/hardware combination, provides capabilities like keyboard programmability, local symbol design, scaling, clipping and rotation. There are many peripherals besides the hardcopy units. For data storage there are cartridge tape recorders, disc cartridges and other mass storage units. Peripherals for recording data on paper include digital pen plotters and dot matrix printers. One commonly attached device is a graphics tablet for digitizing maps, time-velocity pick pairs and other two-dimensional data sets. These can range from 11-in. (0.28 m) square units to a 42 in. by 60 in. (1.1 m by 1.5 m) tablet with between 0.001 and 0.005 inch resolution. There are also screen cross-hair analog dials and joy sticks available for moving cursors and graphic displays interactively.

Industry Examples

Digicon drives the 4014 Tektronix screen with the Logic Sciences HSR-A rasterizer on their VAX-based processing systems. They can display 5 seconds of data on 192 traces on the screen in 8 seconds. At a 4 ms sample rate this is 240,000 data points. The cost of this type of terminal is in the range of $15,000 with a 22-week delivery (1982). However, these systems are not used in practice for production work. Research labs tend to use this type of graphic system much more than processing centers.[5] These terminals could be used for quality control and picking velocity times, but they are "too complicated" for the people who do the work. In general, the oil industry is very slow to implement new ideas. Geophysical contractors present new ideas, but tend to not push them until their customers want the product. Presently there are very few processing programs that are directly tied to graphics display systems.

An exception to the lack of programs tied to softcopy output is the work of Sierra Geophysics. They have developed some 3D ray tracing software that uses several different computer graphics systems for soft copy, including Chromatics and Integraph systems. The examples that follow describe how they use their system. The first step is to define and edit the layers of interest, either as a series of depth cross-sections (Figure 7-1A) or as horizon contour maps (Figure 7-1B). The defined model is uniformly sampled to allow a 3D perspective view (Figure 7-1C). The ray tracing displays (Figure 7-1D and E) give unique visual information about the seismic response over 3D geologic structures. The key results are the synthetic time traces displayed as vertical (Figure 7-1F) or horizontal sections (Figure 7-1G). The computer graphics display of this information show how interactive graphics are enhancing the display of very complex seismic information (Figure 7-1H).

(text continued on page 166)

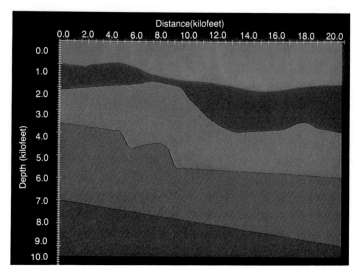

Figure 7-1A. Geologic cross-section at cross line 44, across a continental shelf model. (Courtesy Sierra Geophysics, Inc.)

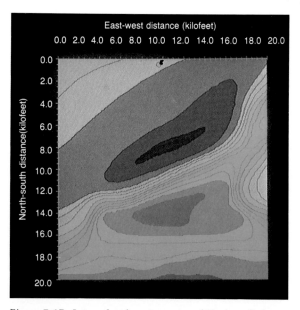

Figure 7-1B. Interpolated contour map of Horizon B showing major structural trap. (Courtesy Sierra Geophysics, Inc.)

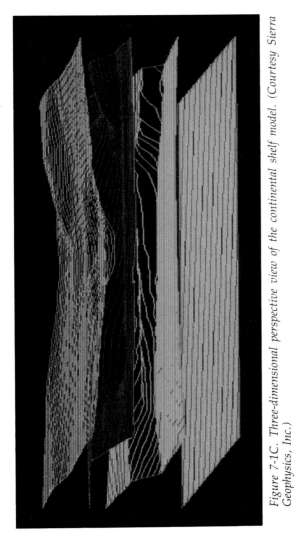

Figure 7-1C. Three-dimensional perspective view of the continental shelf model. (Courtesy Sierra Geophysics, Inc.)

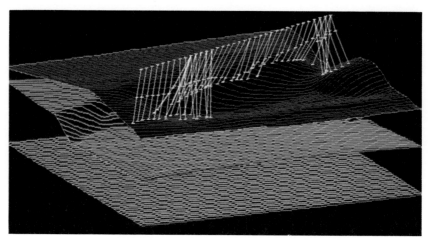

Figure 7-1D. Normal incidence raytracing on strike line from Horizon C. Yellow tick marks indicate ray intersections with layer boundaries and datum plane. (Courtesy Sierra Geophysics, Inc.)

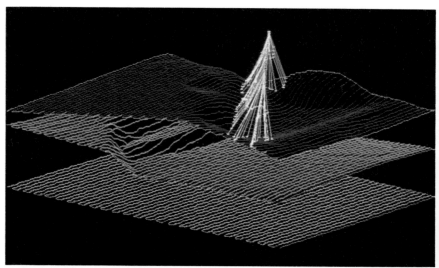

Figure 7-1E. Same line, end view. Note sideswipe raypaths and diffractions from top and bottom of fault. (Courtesy Sierra Geophysics, Inc.)

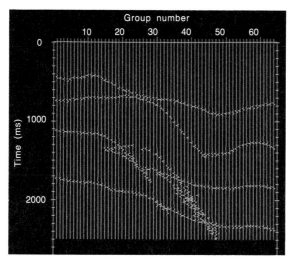

Figure 7-1F. Time section at cross line 44. Note the pinchout between A and B, as well as pull-up on Horizon D. (Courtesy Sierra Geophysics, Inc.)

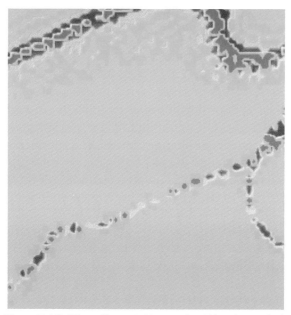

Figure 7-1G. Time slice at 1.10 seconds. Sideswipe arrivals from Horizon B, northern portion Horizon C. (Courtesy Sierra Geophysics, Inc.)

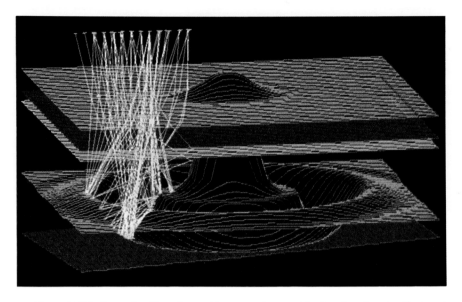

Figure 7-1H. Example of how interactive computer graphics is enhancing the display of complex seismic information. (Courtesy Sierra Geophysics, Inc.)

Man/Machine Interface

Ergonomics, or the physiological interaction between man and machines, has provided major changes in graphics systems over the past few years. These changes can make a significant impact on the willingness of geophysical processors or interpreters to use CRT (cathode ray tube) display screen technology. Advertisements today often stress that a system is human engineered to minimize discomfort. One system has screens that can be adjusted 18 in. in height and swiveled from side-to-side 15°. Screens are shaded or coated to minimize glare. Also, storage tube storage displays are furnished with blue glass light filters for enhanced contrast and safety.[7]

Detachable keyboards that enable users to position them to conform to individual space requirements are becoming more common. There are optimum sizes specified for key size, pressure and spacing. Concave keys with a matte finish minimize reflections and improve operator efficiency. Screens should have variable-brightness control, as well as being unobtrusive and attractive like a telephone or a typewriter.[8]

This same source reports that as terminals become more common in the marketplace, there have been health complaints registered by users. These mostly include short-term effects like blurring, itching and burning eyes, as well as backaches, neck aches and other muscular problems.

The definition of and solution to these problems is improving the work environment of those who spend many hours in front of a CRT. It does take time to set processing parameters and evaluate the results on a CRT, or to do interactive interpretation and map making. If the tool itself is distracting, then the cost benefits of interactive analysis are never evaluated. The introduction of these changes in display technology to seismic data display will bring a change in traditional methods of seismic analysis.

COLOR RASTER GRAPHICS

The state of the art in color raster graphics is rapidly changing. A typical graphics system today usually has more than one RAM (random access memory) memory plane that stores data with a 1:1 tie to the screen pixels (individual picture elements). The medium system has a resolution of 512 by 512 pixels. Screen sizes range from 13 to 25 in. diagonal, which corresponds to between 55 and 30 dots per inch. State of the art resolution for a raster CRT is 1,024 by 1,024 pixels or between 110 and 60 dots per inch for the same range of screen sizes. There are a few prototype systems that are being driven at a resolution of 2,000 by 2,000 pixels.[9]

However, an important difference in comparing CRT resolution to an electrostatic plotter is the fact that raster graphics can vary the intensity of each pixel, while the dots from an electrostatic plotter are either *on* or *off*. Normal intensity variation on a raster display device is 8 bits, or 256 gray levels for each pixel (2 to the 8th power equals 256). To obtain the same intensity variation on a 200-dot-per-inch electrostatic plotter requires that sets of 16 dots (four on the x-axis by four on the y-axis) be set up to represent each pixel element. This does reduce the resolution on the plotter output by a factor of four from 200 dots per inch to 50 "pixels" per inch. It can be said that a CRT with 50 dots per inch resolution and 8 levels of intensity is equivalent to having a hardcopy resolution of 200 dots per inch.

The use of color to display seismic sections is becoming more common, despite the fact that most of the present procedures for generating a color section are complex, time consuming and expensive. However, the potential exists for color graphics to infuse the same type of new vitality to seismic data display as color film did for photography many years ago. Psychological studies have found that color-coded graphs can be perceived 80% more efficiently than black and white graphics.[10] With the proper choice of colors, seismic sections are not only more pleasing to the eye in color, but also are more easily understood. Explorationists are exposed, at least at conventions, to sections displayed in color that enhance certain seismic attributes, like velocity, amplitude, frequency or phase.

There are three general categories of color raster display devices. The lowest priced group is based on four memory planes. One memory plane consists of a 512 by 512 set of one-bit data. Each pixel is either on or off. A two-memory plane system has two bits of information for each pixel. Therefore a four-memory plane system has 2^4 or 16 possible variations for each pixel. This is normally broken down into 16 separate colors or else eight separate colors plus blink (the ability of the pixel to flash on or off). These systems normally cost about $15,000 for a display terminal and have a resolution of 512 by 512.[11] However, they can be set up for a 1,024 by 1,024 screen. In fact, there is a complete spectrum of possible variations between each of these artificial categories.

The second category is typified by the Ramtek 9300, and ranges in price from $25,000 to $40,000. This type of system is based on 12 memory planes, or 4,096 (2^{12}) possible variations in each pixel. Normally in this price range there would be a 4-bit DAC (digital to analog converter) for the red, green and blue electron guns. This results in 16 separate intensities of each of the three primary colors or a total of 4,096 possible colors. With look-up tables (stored reference codes) and wider DACs, this 4,096-color palette can be seleced from a wider range of colors. Most systems at this level have a microprocessor attached. The microprocessor is used to zoom or scale the data and to pan a display window through a larger data set.[11] This processing is not accomplished in anything close to real time. At least one new system, Spectragraphics, uses the microprocessor for polygon fill.[12] This is more common in the much more expensive systems used for flight simulation.

The third category upgrades the display and processing capabilities for finer resolution and more specific types of data processing and manipulation. The price is proportional and can be over $150,000 per unit. This type of system will have up to 24 memory planes. Each color is assigned eight memory planes or 256 pixel variations. An 8-bit DAC is also assigned to each primary color, producing 256 shades per primary color. This results in over 16 million different color combinations that can be assigned to each pixel.[13] This allows very subtle shading, as is seen in displays like the NASA Saturn pictures.

For geophysicists, one of the greatest problems with new color graphics developments is that there are so many options it is difficult to determine what is going to solve the display problem most effectively. Further, if a fairly acceptable solution is arrived at, new developments in graphics technology may soon make it obsolete. For example, many graphics systems are just replacing 16-bit memory chips with 64-bit memory chips as standard products, and 256-bit memory chips are being tested. However, possibly the main reason why more advantage has not been taken of the new color raster graphics technologies is that there is not an off-the-shelf application software package meeting seismic display needs. Also, geophysicists want to use the display to do more than just display the data. There is a need to be able to filter, evaluate seismic attributes, and perform other real time enhancement operations on the display. This is image processing instead of just display technology.

IMAGE PROCESSING

An image processing system is as much a computer as a display terminal. As an example, DeAnza can store an image that is 2,048 by 2,048 and pan through it with either a 512 by 512 or a 1,024 by

1,024 window with 16-bit memory chips. When these are replaced with 64-bit memory chips there should be four times the storage. This system has a pipeline processor with a feedback loop, for real time image processing. Once a data set is displayed, the display is interactively enhanced by the operator without going back to the original numerical definition.

If an image processing system has 12 memory planes, these might be split so that 6 would store the infrared and 6 the visual picture for a Landsat type of analysis. Then using local function buttons or a trackball, the image processing system can be used to overlay the two pictures. For example, the visual picture could be drawn when the infrared intensities are between a specific range, and replaced with the infrared picture otherwise. Interaction between two pictures like this has proven very useful. Another example is subtracting the heat sources recorded on an old picture from a new infrared picture to show new heat sites.[13] Overlaying seismic attributes like velocity, amplitude, frequency and phase promises to provide similar insights for seismologists.

Figure 7-2 is an example of some work done on physical model data using a Ford Aerospace image-processing system. In this example, a 3D survey was shot across a physical model of an amorphous sand body. It was 3D migrated, a horizontal cross-section was extracted, and the resulting data were evaluated on the graphics system. The colors represent changes in the instantaneous phase.[14] The final result of these interactive operations is twofold. The subjective result is the visual image on the screen, which graphically illustrates information not readily apparent on the original unenhanced image. (Objectively, the results can be stored for later recall and manipulation.) It is very useful to have a procedure for making hardcopy pictures of results of interest as image processing proceeds.

VECTOR REFRESH GRAPHICS

Another type of graphics device being evaluated as a tool for exploration geophysics is the vector refresh graphics terminal. These systems have the advantage of creating what appears to be a

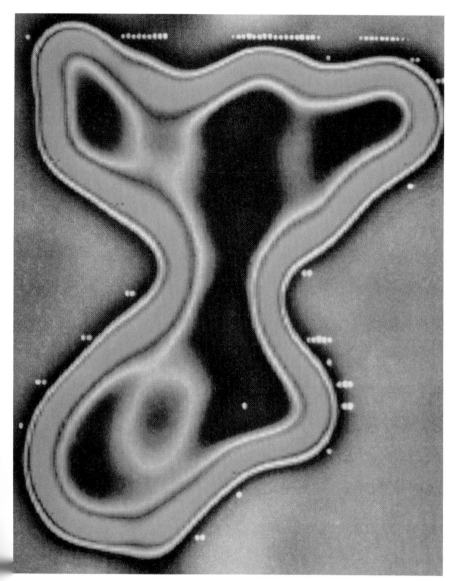

Figure 7-2. Horizontal time-slice seismic section displayed on a Ford Aerospace image processing system. A 3D survey was collected over a physical model of an amorphous sand body, 3D migrated, and displayed as a function of the instantaneous phase.[14]

3D image. The image is really an isometric or perspective drawing that can be rotated, or it can have depth queues (indicators) such as line fading or perspective added to make the drawing appear 3D. The motion parallax accompanying rotation causes the 3D relationships to come alive.[15] Like the raster systems, calligraphic or vector refresh graphics has been used in the CAD/CAM marketplace for some time.

Instead of drawing each horizontal line on the scope face like a raster system does, a line drawing system draws a vector between specified coordinates. The speed at which the stroke generator moves to draw these lines limits the number of vectors that can be drawn before the display begins to flicker. The number of vectors that can be drawn with one of these systems has changed considerably just within the last year. Most of these systems can draw 21,500 3D black-and-white vectors. Vector Automation's Graphicus-80 draws up to 66,000 1/2-word vectors[16] or up to 44,000 1-word vectors. Evans & Sutherlands PS-300 draws about 95,000 2D vectors or 60,000 3D vectors on a screen with 4,096 × 4,096 resolution. The Evans & Sutherland MPS 64-color system is limited to about 12,000 3D vectors, but they have announced a color monitor for the PS-300 that will almost match the number of black and white vectors displayable on the PS-300. All of the colors available on the 1800-color palette can be displayed simultaneously.[17]

Geosource Petty-Ray Research is developing some very interesting applications for these last systems.[18] Figure 7-3 illustrates an interactive velocity analysis program. The user first loads a standard demultiplexed field tape. Then from the display console a record is requested. This is displayed on the left hand side of the screen in about the time it takes to read the tape. Stacking velocities are picked, the Dix interval velocity immediately calculated and displayed, and NMO (normal moveout) correction applied to see if the velocity picks are correct. The velocities can be interactively repicked and NMO reapplied immediately.

Because of the limited number of vectors that can be drawn, some data reduction has been needed to efficiently use this type of graphics system. One technique is to only display a small temporal window of interest, where the window follows an event of interest across the seismic section. This is illustrated in Figure 7-4A. In this example, an event was picked using a digitizing tablet. The in-

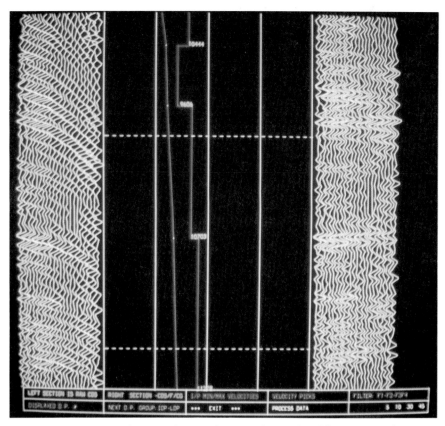

Figure 7-3. Interactive velocity analysis. A field record is displayed from a magnetic tape (left yellow), a stacking velocity is interactively picked (red), the Dix interval velocity is instantly calculated and displayed (blue), and NMO applied to check the velocity picks (right yellow).[18] (Courtesy Geosource, Petty-Ray Geophysical Division.)

terpretation of the same event on a parallel line 100 meters away was connected and the results rotated to show the cross-dip of the structure (Figure 7-4B).[18] Because this type of display device draws 3D pictures, it is possible to display and rotate a "3D corkscrew" complex trace. Figure 7-5 is a 1980 example of a display of a few samples of a complex trace. The complex trace appears to be a corkscrew in x, y, and z. By projecting the real portion of the trace onto an x, y plane, the standard wiggle trace appears.[19] Eventually, interactive graphics will make complex trace analysis much easier and more useful.

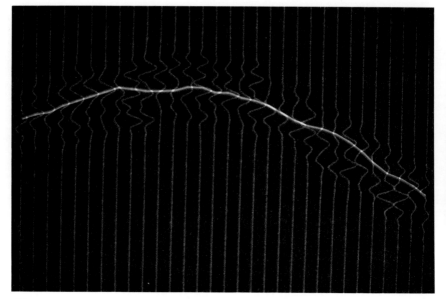

Figure 7-4A. Interpreting wiggle traces on a color vector refresh graphics scope.[18] (Courtesy Geosource, Petty-Ray Geophysical Division.)

RASTER VECTOR COMBINATIONS

Several ways have been developed to merge the capabilities of raster and vector scopes. The most extravagant and expensive are the flight simulator systems. The author is aware of two systems that provide interesting capabilities for geophysical data display.

The first is the Adage 4145 with a Raster Segment Generator (RSG). In this system, a firmware package packs up to 16 data values into each memory word, and the picture is displayed in raster format. This increases the number of vectors that can be displayed before flicker by a factor of better than 10. There is one vector displayed for each sample. For example, with 1-bit resolution (each sample is a dot, either on or off), 1,000 samples on 240 traces can be displayed in one RSG frame before flicker. Figure 7-6 is an example of a portion of a seismic section from the overthrust

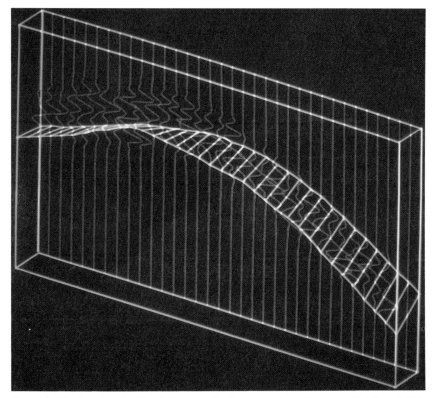

Figure 7-4B. Rotation in 3D of the cross-dip interpretation of two parallel lines 1,000 meters apart.[18] (Courtesy Geosource, Petty-Ray Geophysical Division.)

zone in Wyoming's Wind River basin at 3-bit resolution. This means that each sample is represented by a horizontal vector that is off, or up to 7 units (dots) in length.

Because the Adage is a vector refresh graphics system, the display response time is very quick. Therefore, when another section is requested, it appears on the screen as fast as the function switch is acknowledged. This allows a stack of horizontal or vertical sections to be animated in movie form on the computer graphics terminal.[20]

The amount of data (percentage of the total section) that is within the display window varies as a function of the format of the display (1-bit, 2-bit, up to 16-bit). At 16-bit resolution only 1 trace is displayed in a single frame of RSG memory storage. A more common display would be 120 traces displayed at 2-bit resolution. Using a

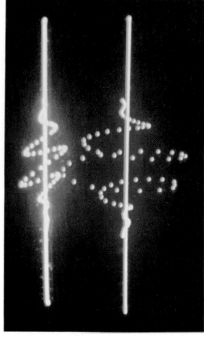

Figure 7-5. Projection of the real component from 280 samples of a complex trace.[19]

triple buffering algorithm, the display window can be interactively moved across a much larger section of data, either horizontal or vertical sections (Figure 7-7). In fact, all available disc memory can be filled with preformatted seismic data, organized in RSG frames, and then the display window interactively moved across the section in either direction to follow events of interest.[21] If there is a data volume preformatted for display, the window can be moved to parallel sections in front, in back, above, or beneath the one displayed, with no response delay. Another capability that has been illustrated with this system is to animate through mixed displays of horizontal and vertical sections (Figure 7-8).[22] This allows an interpreter to visually evaluate spatial and temporal relationships simultaneously.

The other hybrid system is the Megatek Whizzard 7200. This is also a vector picture processor, but the display tube is raster. The data from the digital vector generator is dumped into double-buffered raster memory planes. The raster display is updated from one of the memory buffers. This means there is no flicker or display delay during picture processing.

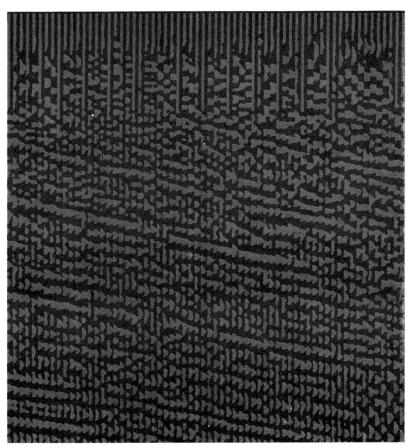

Figure 7-6. Display of 1,000 samples on 64 traces from a Wyoming Wind River basin overthrust seismic section using the raster segment generator at 3-bit resolution.[20]

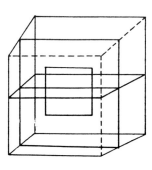

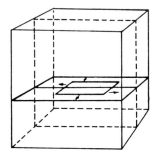

Panimator vertical
section window

Panimator time-slice
window movement

Figure 7-7. Panimator display planes.

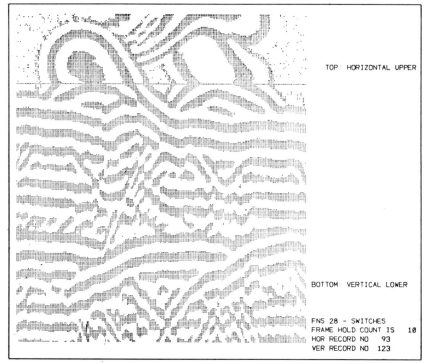

Figure 7-8. Animation can also be done with mixed displays of horizontal and vertical sections.[22] *In this example, the top portion of the display is a time-slice section and the bottom is a vertical section across the SALGLF model.*

The system can be configured with a calligraphic vector generator, which removes the raster capability and makes it a line drawing device.[23] This makes it possible to have very rapid rotation of the line drawings. However, rapid dynamics is not usually required for most geophysical applications. Figure 7-9 shows a color raster seismic benchmark that can be rapidly rotated in 3D space.

FUTURE GRAPHICS DEVELOPMENTS

Many explorationists feel that the ideal computer controlled display system will be as large as a wall and at the same resolution. The author thinks that readily available computer graphics systems can accomplish the same thing, if there is application software. This

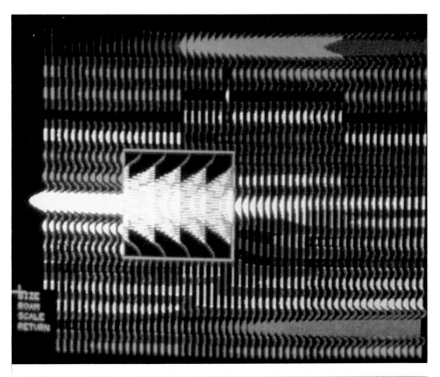

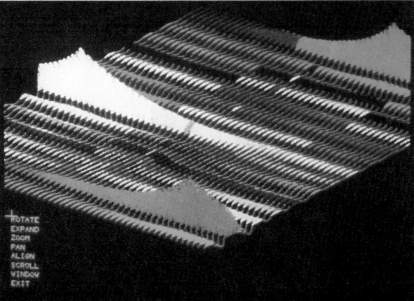

Figure 7-9. Examples of a 2D and 3D color vectorized raster displays of synthetic seismic data.[23] (Courtesy Megatek Corp.)

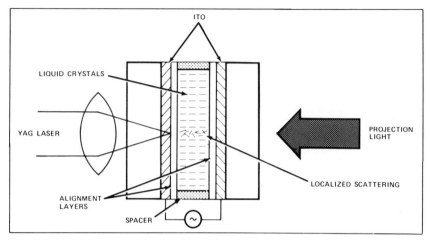

Figure 7-10. The structure of a smectic liquid crystal light valve. ITO = Indium tin oxide coating. (After R. Tsai et al.[25] Courtesy Librascope, a division of Singer Co.)

needs to specifically include the capabilities of zooming in or out on the data and translating the display window along any axis of a 3D data volume. However, there has been a large-scale computer display system developed for the U.S. military that is being integrated into an interpretation work station by at least one company, The Denver Processing Center.[24] The display unit is a laser-addressed, liquid-crystal, large-screen projection display.

The display system is made by Librascope, a division of the Singer Company. It consists of two smectic liquid-crystal light valves (Figure 7-10), which are selectively thermally addressed by a single laser. Each light valve is capable of generating 2048 by 2048 addressable pixels within a 1 in. by 1 in. data format.[25] This means that 8×10^6 pixels are available for forward or rear projection to a screen that can range in size from 1 m to 5 m square. The display can have 4 colors (Figure 7-11) with a resolution of 2500 lines per inch on the liquid crystal light valve. With 48× magnification this gives a resolution equivalent to about 50 dots per inch on the display screen. Note that the initial resolution is the same as the state of the art in CRT technology, which can also be employed in a projection system. The liquid-crystal system can generate alpha-numerics, graphics, and symbols by raster scanning and random vectors.

IBM research has developed a similar large information capacity display (LICD). Their LICD permits the simultaneous presentation

Figure 7-11. Example of display possible using liquid crystal light valve of Figure 7-10. (Courtesy Librascope, a division of Singer Co.)

of a maximum of 8,000 by 8,000, or 64 million, pixel elements.[26] The information is written on a liquid crystal cell, which measures 100 cm by 100 cm (4 in. by 4 in.). This system can provide a resolution of 200 pixels per inch on a 1-meter-square rear projection screen. It takes 80 seconds to write a complete screen of data. The maximum writing rate is limited by the mechanical scanner, the number of lasers, the controller interface data rate, and the host/controller link data rate. For example, by increasing the number of lasers to 128 and keeping the present mechanical system, the image could be written in 20 seconds. One nice characteristic is the ability to selectively erase and rewrite a portion of the image. This would allow the "zooming in" on a portion of a seismic section of interest. The display also has a pointing function that allows the interactive picking of seismic sections. The pointing function is implemented by an invisible light beam that sweeps over the surface of the screen. Interruption of the beam by any pointer (pencil, finger, etc.) defines the center of the pointer position within 0.5 mm (20 mil).[26] Prototypes of these systems are being tested for seismic display (1983), but expense will probably inhibit early widespread use.

Another project that could impact upon interactive graphics display of seismic data is the work of a new movie company, Digital Production, Inc. They have purchased a Cray-1 computer specifically to put high-resolution data (6,000 by 4,500 24-bit pixels) directly on film. The first project is a movie entitled Star-Fighters (contract awarded July 1982).[26]

There are certainly other projects on the horizon that will provide explorationists with a new "looking glass" for rapidly evaluating the volumes of data that are stacking up. This includes development of reciprocity relationships that should permeate computing, but do not. Terms like computer vision, robotics, voice synthesis and speech recognition promise to move from science fiction to application. Also, the work that is being done in pattern recognition and artificial intelligence is bound to reduce the data an interpreter must evaluate in order to select a drilling location.[28]

HARDCOPY

A basic requirement for an interactive graphics system for geophysical analysis is that there be an easy and efficient way to make hardcopies of the screen display. This is one reason that the Tektronix tubes are so widely used. They have a fast, accurate, easily used, screen-to-hardcopy unit. Devices like the Adage and the Megatek can be directly interfaced to an electrostatic plotter. With the rasterizer this is a fast process. However, without the rasterizer, a long time is needed to plot out the vector files.

One milestone in producing color hardcopies is the development of the ACT-1 ink jet color copier from Advanced Color Technology of Chelmsford, Massachusetts. The system is about the size of a typewriter and weighs 40 lbs (18 kg). The resolution is 85 dots/inch horizontal and up to 140 dots/inch vertical. A good quality 8½ by 11-inch (3.3 by 4.3 −cm) hardcopy of a color display, with 7 solid colors and up to 125 color shades, can be generated in a couple of minutes.

The best way to obtain a hardcopy of a color seismic display off of any monitor is with a Polaroid camera. Dunn, Ramtek and others make camera units that will do this. Slides and movies can also be made with proper camera equipment. Other methods to obtain hardcopies include the use of color pen plotters that can be interfaced to a terminal, or full color digital dot matrix printers, which currently are being developed.

One of the best potential storage mediums for horizontal section movies is video tape, whereby one can go directly from the computer to the tape. There are resolution problems with the best video systems on the market in 1982. Because of the bandwidth limitation of video recording there are restrictions as to how much data can be stored. The standard U.S. format limits the picture to about 480 by 380 pixels per frame. Research prototype video recording systems, with 1,000 by 1,000 pixel resolution, are being developed. There are also black and white electron beam recording systems available that go from digital form directly to microfilm or slides. Unfortunately, making hardcopies is an area that does not have a nice, clean answer as to what is the best method.

GRAPHICS JUSTIFICATION

New display technologies have many potential applications in exploration seismology. The need to have a more efficient and accurate method of handling the data volumes being utilized today justifies developing this technology. There are several factors that, when tied together, point to graphics as having a major effect on exploration seismology over the next few years, primarily because of all the new developments occurring in graphics technology. The new raster, vector and image processing systems are at a stage where only proper software application packages are needed to justify their use.

It has been known for many years that there is a tremendous increase in efficiency using an interactive over a batch system. Computer scientists have quantified this improvement,[29] however, there needs to be a detailed evaluation of how interactive techniques affect a processing and an interpretation environment. Is there an increase in the accuracy of workers? Does interactive seismic display make it easier to visualize data relationships in building an interpretation? Is it easier to visualize a complex 3D geological feature if it is viewed in 3D? How much improvement is there in measurable quantities such as interpretation time? If interpreters can move through a data volume at will, does it aid the understanding of data interrelationships? How can the apprenticeship time be shortened in the training of "good" interpreters?

Interactive graphic systems that include a display device with an interpretation package and the raw data in storage have the advantage of allowing an interpreter to rapidly walk a manager or a partner through the critical parts of the interpretation. In addition, it is easier to store data digitally for recall, updating, or even for transferring from one office to another. Digital data transfer can be by satellite, phone, tape, disc, etc.

Because this technology does not have widespread use, it has not been *proven* cost effective. Many still ask if development costs can be offset by the decrease in the manhours required for geophysical analysis using an interactive system. It is obviously effective to have interpretations keep up with data acquisition and processing, and interactive interpretation techniques do help in this area, especially in regards to keeping up with 3D surveys. If there is any increase in the number of successful wells, as a result of better interpretations, then the development of interactive geophysical analysis techniques *is* cost justified.

SUMMARY

Computer graphics technology has made tremendous advances because of the CAD/CAM market. These advances have placed this technology on the doorstep of geophysical exploration techniques. Although there are many reasons why color raster and vector graphics are not used more widely in our industry today, data handling needs and the necessity to stay abreast of seismic data collection and processing advancements point to this as being an area of major progress over the next few years. As these developments are cost justified, they will have an accelerated acceptance.

References

1. Nelson, H. R., Jr. "Trends in Multichannel Seismic Recording Systems," *World · Oil*, pp. 135-142, Nov. 1981.
2. Nelson, H. R., Jr., "New Vector Super Computers Promote Seismic Advancements, *World Oil*, pp. 155-160, Jan. 1982.
3. Nelson, H. R., Jr., "3D Seismic Techniques Aid Exploration, Development," *World Oil*, pp. 115-120, Dec. 1981.
4. Information Display Products, Tektronix brochure, 1979.
5. Limbaugh, R. S., Digicon Geophysical, Houston, Texas, personal communication, 1982.
6. 3D Ray Tracing Software, Sierra Geographysics brochure, 1982.
7. Product Specification, M & S Computing brochure, 1980.
8. Raftery and Keener, "Providing Terminal Comfort," *Mini-Micro Systems*, pp. 119-126, Aug. 1981.
9. Kinsella, K. J., Spectra Graphics, personal communication, 1982.
10. Calev, F., "Enhancing Comprehension with Color, *Mini-Micro Systems*, pp. 139-144, Aug. 1981.
11. Tashbar, P. W., DeAnza Systems, San Diego, California, personal communication, 1982.
12. SPEC 1000 System, Spectragraphics brochure, 1981.
13. Uselton, S. P., University of Houston Computer Science Department, personal communication, 1982.
14. Gardner, G. H. F., University of Houston Allied Geographical Laboratory, Houston, Texas, personal communication, 1981.
15. Nelson, H. R., Jr., Hilterman, F. J., and Gardner, G. H. F., "Introduction to Interactive 3D Interpretation," *Oil & Gas Journal*, V. 79, No. 40, pp. 106-125, 1981.

16. Graphicus-80, Vector Automation pamphlet, 1981.
17. Sovelius, P. F., Evans and Sutherland, Houston, Texas, personal communication, July 1982.
18. Massell, W. F., Winningham, D. J. and Nelson, H. R., Jr., "Interactive Geophysical Analysis with 3D Color Graphics," SEG Convention, L.A., California, paper 7.4, 1981. (See abstract, *Geophysics*, V. 47, No. 4, p. 469, 1982.)
19. Nelson, H. R., Jr., Hilterman, F. J., and Gardner, G. H. F., "Introduction to Interactive 3D Interpretation," SAL Semi-Annual Progress Review, V. 5, pp. 149-192, May 1980.
20. Nelson, H. R., Jr., Gardner, T. N., and Hilterman, F. J., "Interpretation of Physical Model Tank Data with the Raster Segment Generator," SEG Convention, L.A., Calif., paper S18.7, 1981. (See abstract, *Geophysics*, V. 47, No. 4, pp. 497-498, 1982.)
21. Nelson, H. R., Jr., *et al*, "Interactively Displaying Data From a Disc Full of Seismic Traces," SAL Annual Progressive Review, V. 8, pp. 368-384, 1981.
22. Verm, R. W., and Nelson, H. R., Jr., "Interactively Mixing the Display of Horizontal and Vertical Seismic Sections," SAL Semi-Annual Progress Review, V. 9, pp. 409-421, 1982.
23. Head, D., Megatek, Dallas, Texas, personal communication, 1981.
24. Teagland, E. R., "3D Seismic Methods, Turnaround Time and What the Future Holds," presentation at Norwegian Petroleum Society's Conference on 3D Seismic Techniques, Cristiansand, S., Norway, March 8-10, 1982.
25. Tsai, R., *et al*, "A High Density Multicolor Liquid Crystal Display," preprint from Librascope, 1981.
26. Cheroff, G., IBM, San Jose, California, personal communication, 1982.
27. Wortham, J., Cray Research, Inc., Houston, Texas, personal communication, 1982.
28. Hildebrand, H.A., Landmark Graphics Corp., personal communication, Houston, Texas, 1982.
29. Sackman, H., *Man Computer Problem Solving—Experimental Evaluation of Time-Sharing and Batch Processing*, Auerback Publishers, Inc., New York, 272 p., 1970.

CHAPTER 8

True 3D
Display Devices

The earth is three-dimensional; hence, it is logical that 3D display devices will become aids to subsurface interpretation. Technological advances are providing a new generation of display systems and techniques that provide a true 3D view of data volumes. Many of these methods have been developed for application in other fields, such as chemistry and medicine. However, active research is still underway in search of the best approach to displaying computer generated geophysical/geological data.

This chapter goes beyond today's state of the art in computer graphics display[1] to describe true 3D display devices and techniques that are being evaluated in various research laboratories around the world. These advances are closely tied to the expected application of 3D display devices as interpretational tools for explorationists.

The three-dimensional display of data sets is needed in many different scientific projects. Research areas that are seeking true 3D display techniques include: medicine, with applications, such as the displaying of data from ultrasound echo scanners,[2] computed tomographic scanners (cat scans) like the Mayo Clinic Dynamic Spacial Reconstructor,[3] radiographs,[4] shadowgraphs[5] and nuclear emmision;[6] chemistry, through the displaying of molecules and molecular interactions;[7] biology, through reconstructing nerve cell interconnections;[8] meteorology, by illustrating multi-dimensional meteorological data fields;[9,10] traffic control, by displaying radar and sonar images in 3D for air traffic control or submarine location;

187

mathematics, by illustrating multi-dimensional mathematical information like curves and surfaces; geology, through studying earthquake epicenter locations in 3D[11] and, of course, reflection seismology, by evaluating volumes of seismic data in relation to well and geologic information.[12]

Similarly, there is great interest in using this technology for the entertainment and advertising industries. Possible applications range from 3D movies, to 3D home TV, to 3D video arcades or even 3D photography.

In the early 1970s, the field of holography seemed to offer spectacular promise for meeting these more general applications as well as the scientific needs. However, there are basic characteristics of laser holography that limit widespread application.[13] For instance, laser holography produces a one-color scene. There is also the speckle effect, which the Hungarian-born inventor Dennis Gabor once called "holographic enemy number one."[14] That is, at the wavelength of visible light, even the smoothest surface appears bumpy, and the result is a speckle that dazzles the eye and further detracts from the realism of the image. Further, display size is a problem, because a large hologram requires a large, expensive laser, and these can damage the human eye. However, the biggest problem from the scientific side is that holograms are a photographic plate, meaning that the display cannot interact with a digital computer data base. All in all, there will need to be major breakthroughs before holography will provide a method of interactively working with a volume of seismic data. Currently an active participant in the advancement of holography is Dr. Stephen A. Benton,[15] senior scientist at Polaroid Corp.'s Research Lab, Cambridge, Mass., who has put together a history of the conceptual evolution of 3D imaging techniques, called "Similar Visions," for the New York Museum of Holography.

While the search for a true 3D display device for interactive analysis of seismic data volumes has not yet provided a satisfactory answer, a whole range of devices exists that have the potential of helping to solve the problem. These methods range from a $35 pair of parabolic mirrors to computer driven systems with unlimited price tags. The remainder of this chapter summarizes these developments and describes how they are presently being implemented.

Figure 8-1. In this simple 3D imaging device, called the Mirage, two parabolic mirrors face each other and are separated by the distance of their common focal lengths. Note that the hole being pointed to acts as a mirrored surface, and that even the imaged object, the knob also pointed to, is actually resting in the bottom of Mirage although it appears to sit above the device (See Figure 8-2).

PARABOLIC MIRRORS

Mirage is the trade name of a novelty toy made by Opti-Gone Associates, Woodland Hills, Calif. This simple imaging device consists of two identical parabolic mirrors facing each other and separated by a distance equal to the common focal length (Figure 8-1). The imaging principle involved is illustrated in Figure 8-2. The image in the base of the mirrors appears to be sitting in space.

Most other 3D display devices are more complicated than Mirage and create images in virtual, or non-invadable, space. However, by displaying a computer-created virtual image at the base of a set of parabolic mirrors, the image is moved into real space where it can be interacted with.[16]

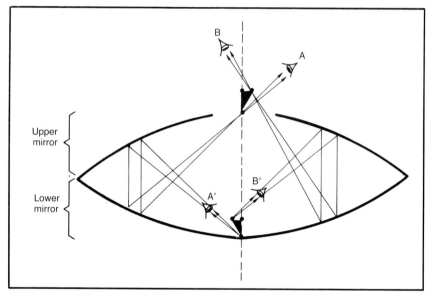

Figure 8-2. The real triangular object to be imaged is located at the bottom of the lower mirror. An upgoing cone of rays issuing from the bottom point of the triangle takes the path shown and reconverges at the exact center of the upper mirror parabola. Because the mirror allows the viewer at A to see the same diverging ray cone as a viewer at A', there is a 180° rotation of the image. (After A. L. Simpson.[16])

Dr. Simpson, at the University of Houston's Cullen Image Processing Lab (IPL), has started working on one practical application for Mirage. This has involved installing it in a box with its top flush with the viewing hole. Stable pointers are then inserted into the image, in order to determine an individual's accuracy in depth positioning as a function of viewing distance. This may help to design 3D interaction algorithms, as well as in selection of personnel for work with data volumes.

For many years, earth scientists have worked with similar "illusions" in the form of air photo stereo pairs. An example of stereo air photos is shown in Figure 8-3. The relief of Zion Canyon in southwestern Utah appears to come out of the flat page, when these two pictures are fused in the viewer's mind.[17] Some people cannot fuse stereo pairs to see a three-dimensional picture. Simple stereoscopes, which can be picked up in most university bookstores, help in fusing stereo pairs. (The principle is the same as that used in the stereo movies). It is interesting to note that if there is

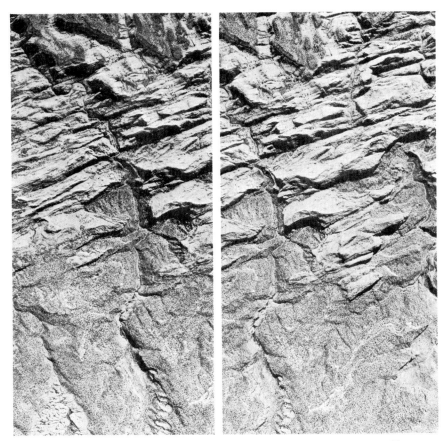

Figure 8-3. Stereo aerial photograph of Zion National Park in southwestern Utah.[17] To the trained eye the plateaus seem to be above the printed page when the pictures are fused together by the brain. A simple stereoscope helps untrained eyes fuse these pictures. (After Hamblin and Howard.[17])

rotational movement of a data volume, there is little problem visualizing 3D because of the accompanying motion parallax.[18,19]

PROJECTION IMAGING

It seems that medical researchers have been attacking the problem of true 3D display of data volumes longer than geoscientists. At least many of the 3D display techniques developed have been for studying medical data volumes.

For example, when an x-ray is taken a "radiograph" is made on photographic film. Each point on the radiograph is the integral of the x-ray density (the linear attenuation coefficient) along the path connecting the x-ray source and the point on the detector. These projection "pictures" cannot be interpreted when the image of the structure cannot be distinguished from the background. One method of removing this super-position is to selectively opacify the desired anatomy.

Another method is computed tomography (CT), which uses projection information from many angles of "view" around the body to numerically generate a 2D slice through the body. Because superposition is minimized in CT scans, this method is useful in distinguishing hidden structure, even though the spatial resolution and noise characteristics of cross-sectional images are inferior to that of radiographs.[20] A stack of these CT scans results in a data volume that needs to be evaluated, very similar to a volume of seismic data.[21]

Lowell Harris, at the Mayo Clinic, developed one method of accomplishing this using numerical reprojection of data from a volume of CT scans to create a projection image. Figure 8-4 summarizes this procedure. By making 2D digital "radiographs" of the reconstructed volume at different viewing angles, the volume can be viewed as a stereo pair, or put on video and rotated for motion parallax.[18] Because the CT data volume is digital, it can be manipulated to overcome superposition prior to being reprojected. These enhancement methods are referred to as selective "tissue dissolution" and non-effacive numerical "dissection."[20] In other words, the radiologist is able to use numerically those fundamental medical procedures used by pathologists to cut, peel, and dissect the data volume for detailed analysis.

Explorationists face a similar problem. To study the application of these procedures, a volume of physical model data[22] was evaluated using these techniques.[23] Figure 8-5 is a stereoscopic photograph of that physical model taken from an overhead position. The model consists of five thin plexiglass lenses at various heights above a plexiglass base plate. The model was placed in the Seismic Acoustic Laboratory (SAL) modeling tank and a volume of common-offset seismic traces collected. The trace spacing and line spacing was the same so that each trace represented one square on a surface grid.

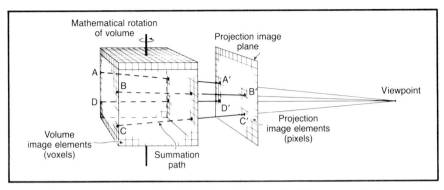

Figure 8-4. Picture elements (voxels) of the volume on the left are numerically summed along projection paths (four representative paths shown) to form the picture elements (pixels) of the two-dimensional projection image in the center. When the resulting digital image is displayed, it is as though the observer views the volume image from the viewpoint on the right. (Reproduced from SEG Reprint,[22] Courtesy L.D. Harris, "Identification of the Optimal Orientation of Oblique Sections Through Multiple Parallel CT Images," Journal of Computer Assisted Tomography)

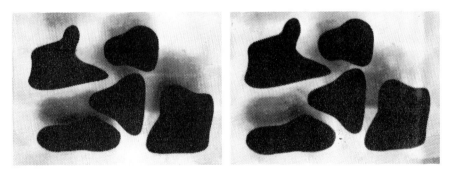

Figure 8-5. Stereoscopic photograph of a physical model with five plexiglass lenses raised above a plexiglass base. The highest lens is in the bottom right corner, they stairstep down to the top left corner lens, and the bottom left and top right lenses are lowest and are at the same elevation.[23]

The raw data was projected at two different viewing angles to form the stereo pair shown in Figure 8-6. Notice how the diffractions make the data appear to be out of focus. After the 3D migration of this raw data volume, the image projection results in Figure 8-7.[24] This is a projection of the amplitude envelope from the Hilbert Transformation of the migrated data set, and is a good example of how 3D migration will "focus" a data volume. If these were sand lenses in an oil bearing sequence, it would be easy to specify drilling sites.

A video rotation sequence of projections of the same data volume gives an even clearer view of the 3D relationships. However, this movement cannot be reproduced on the printed page. The rotation sequences do give additional credence to the use of vector refresh graphics as a tool for evaluating 3D data volumes.[1,19] It is interesting that the Department of Biological Sciences at Columbia University has been using vector graphics systems since the early 1970s to visualize biologically active molecules in three dimensions. This group has developed automatic contouring and picking programs that contour off of cross-sectional photographs, and if the contour is not within acceptable tolerances the automatic procedure stops and alerts an operator.[8] Motion is also key in the success of flight simulator systems as a training tool for pilots.

3D DISPLAYS FROM FILM

Stereoscopic comprehension of a 3D picture can be accomplished without having to have a stereoscope or the rotational movement of the object. One way is to use James Butterfield's Autostereoscopic Film Display.[25] In this system, cameras are used to record a stereo pair on film. The two pictures are projected by separate projectors onto a Fresnel lens screen, which is optically equivalent to a large diameter convex lens. The viewer positions his head so that each eye perceives only one of the images. The brain fuses these images as a single 3D picture. With a 2½-in. diameter projector lens, the viewer has a viewing window of 2½ in. left, right, up-and-down, and about 18 in. in-and-out of the screen. This viewing window can be greatly increased using a screen made of

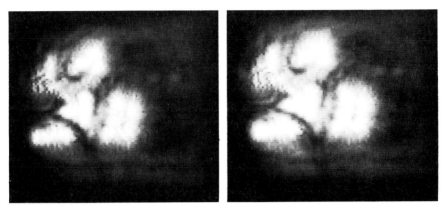

Figure 8-6. A stereoscopic projection of a volume of unprocessed seismic data over the physical model from Figure 8-5. Note the unfocused appearance caused by the diffractions.[23]

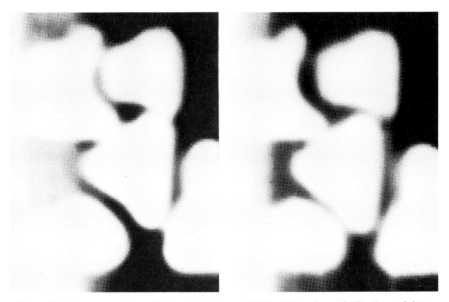

Figure 8-7. A stereoscopic projection of a volume of Hilbert Transformed 3D migrated data from the physical model in Figure 8-5. Note the focusing effect of migration compared to Figure 8-6.[24]

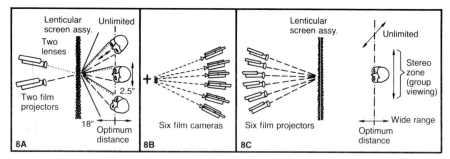

Figure 8-8. The autostereoscopic film projection of a stereo pair on a lenticular screen (A). Note that the viewer can move his head and still see the stereo pair. Using multiple cameras (B) and the same number of projectors (C) the stereo zone can be expanded for group viewing. (Courtesy Jim Butterfield.)

lenticlular lens, as is shown in Figure 8-8A. This configuration will repeat that stereo view for every 2½-in. movement of the observer.[25] This same procedure can be expanded for group viewing by using multiple cameras to film an object (Figure 8-8B). The same number of projectors is used to create a 3D image that can be viewed by several people simultaneously (Figure 8-8C). It seems reasonable that the same procedures can be used with multiple computer-controlled CRTs (cathode ray tubes).

Another device that uses film to produce a 3D display is called the synthalyzer.[26] This system uses a set of 60-70 coordinated sections of a specimen recorded on a 16mm film strip. The film is mounted on a transparent drum that revolves at about 1,200 rpm. A strobe light freezes the projected image above a stepped cylinder with translucent Archimedes spiral segments. The result is similar to that observed with the parabolic mirrors. There are also two main sets of controls, as decribed by de Montebello, that are used to study hidden details of a reconstructed specimen. The first is an optical dissector that basically blocks portions of the display. The second is an electronic chopper that allows successive removal and isolation of the projected layers. These can be used independently or in conjunction. Dr. Budinger, Donner Laboratory and University of California at Berkeley, described an interesting variation of this concept, assuming money is no problem.[27] A shutter could be rapidly moved in front of a set of 18 images on two CRTs. As the shutter passes, each image is passed through a series of glass lenses and is reflected off of a rotating silvered cylinder. The optics is set up so that a real image is created under computer control.

BEAM-SPLITTING TECHNIQUES

Dennis Ricks, of Ricks Research, Ltd., in Louisville, Colo., has demonstrated a new 3D television display that uses multiple CRTs and beam splitting mirrors to place the pictures in proper 3D space. Cross-sectional images are optically stacked by the beam splitters so that they appear one behind the other to form a composite three-dimensional image. Lenses are used to project the 3D image towards a viewing window. These lenses can also enlarge the image. More than five prototypes have been built, with image characteristics that range from medium resolution black and white to high resolution color.[28] A prototype system has been built with 16 backlighted transparencies illustrating a scene from the Apollo moon landing. The same type of lens configuration could be used with CRTs, but it is more expensive than using backlighted transparencies.

In working with a simple black and white version, it becomes obvious that with more than three unedited seismic sections it is impossible to recognize events because of superposition. If interactive terminals are incorporated and numerical "pathology" techniques are developed, this type of device has promise as a 3D interactive interpretation tool.

Dr. Stephen Pizer, at the University of North Carolina in Chapel Hill, had a similar research project. He used optical tunnels to multiplex hardcopy pictures and create a 3D image.[29] However, it was found that lenses provide a better solution than do the optical tunnels and that interaction with the display, not provided by the tunnels, is very important. Therefore, this research has been put on a back burner.

ROTATING LIGHT-EMITTING DIODES

One of the most unique 3D display devices was developed at the Massachusetts Institute of Technology Innovation Center. This system is based on rotating a two-dimensional array of red, light-emitting diodes (LEDs). The first tested and planned application for this device is to display x-ray tomographs in 3D. The intention is not to replace present 2D display techniques, but to provide a method to enhance the physician's interpretation of the data volume being worked with.[30] These are the same steps that must be followed in order to interactively interpret seismic volumes, i.e., to develop methods to work effectively with 2D slices on CRTs and then to add 3D display techniques to these procedures to enhance interpretation.

The concept is to use the motion of rotating a 2D image in space to create the third dimension. Static images result as the red LEDs are turned on at the same position in space while the array of lights is rapidly rotated. Each position, P, is defined in the usual cylindrical coordinate system as is shown in Figure 8-9A. The three coordinates defining p are: r, the radius; z, the height; and θ, the angle from a reference plane. In the laboratory prototype, there is a 2-inch square panel with 4,096 red LEDs, with a linear density of 32 diodes per inch. The array is visible from only one side. With the axis of rotation in the middle of the square array, the image volume swept out is a cylinder two inches high and two inches in diameter. Even with this small prototype, there is a large amount of data needed to construct a complete image. The number of points in the

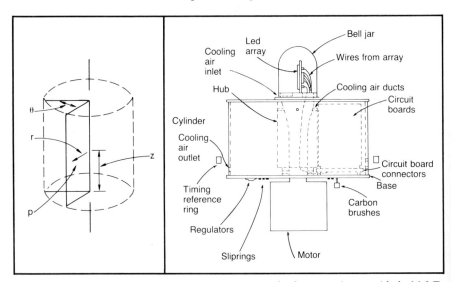

Figure 8-9. In A the cylindrical coordinate system used to locate a point, p, with the M.I.T. rotating diode display device: r is the radius; z is the height; and θ is the angle from a reference plane. B shows the mechanical assembly of the device. (Courtesy M.I.T. Innovation Center.)

2D array and the large number of discrete angular positions that images are to be displayed at for a flicker-free presentation requires large data transfer bandwidth.[30] The mechanical configuration is described in Figure 8-9B. The electronics have been worked out and the patent assigned to Tri-Vi Corporation (1982).

In view of the potential applications to seismic display, it will be interesting watch the development of this system, as larger commercial versions are built. Plans are being made to build a larger device with an array diameter of six or eight inches. This will be rotated 20 times per second to decrease flicker. The use of multicolor LEDs to make a color display is also being evaluated.[31] Because the display is non-invadable, there has been talk that the system might be placed in the base of a set of parabolic mirrors.[16] The would allow the analyst to work with the 3D image.

VIBRATING MIRRORS

The most advanced, commercially available true 3D display devices are based on creating a volume of virtual images with a varifocal or vibrating mirror. This display volume is created by synchronizing the displays on a high resolution CRT with the movement of the mirror. The mirror is only moved about 4 cm (peak to peak) at its center, but the optics move the image position extremes about 35 cm.[32] Because of distortion, the normal virtual image volume evaluated with a 30-cm diameter mirror is an 18-cm cube.

There are two closely related methods of using the vibrating mirrors. The original patent was for a system that has a flexible mirror. This system, known as the Volume Viewer, has a been worked on at the University of Utah Research Institute for several years now by Dr. Steve Johnson and Dr. Brent Baxter.[33] The mirror for this system is simply silvered Mylar film that is stretched over a large hoop. The mirror is moved by a standard woofer speaker. Several prototype systems have been developed and considerable software is available for the system to aid in displaying radiographs and other 3D medical data volumes. This software allows rotation of data volumes, etc.

The other system, called the SpaceGraph (Figure 8-10), was developed by Dr. Larry Sher of Bolt, Beranek, and Newman, Inc.,

Cambridge, Mass., and has been licensed to Genisco computers. Several systems, four of which are in exploration research labs, were delivered in mid-1982.

Besides the fact that additional software drivers are being integrated into the SpaceGraph during manufacturing, the biggest difference between the SpaceGraph and the Volume Viewer is that the SpaceGraph has a solid, and yet flexible mirror. Its display characteristics include a virtual image volume of up to 25 (x-axis) by 20 (y-axis) by 30 (z-axis) cm. There can be 32,768 points displayed in graphics mode, and 262,144 voxels displayed in image mode.[34] A voxel is a volume picture element, and was named by Dr. Sher.[18] Figure 8-11 (A and B) is a sequence of pictures taken off of the vibrating mirror. Unfortunately, the three-dimensionality of the display cannot be reproduced photographically.

Dr. Pizer at the University of North Carolina has developed another varifocal mirror system that is based on a standard color raster graphics display.[29] This system is routinely displaying CT images. Working with this system, Pizer found that there is still much to learn about gray scale before tackling the complex problem of color 3D display. The angle that a 3D object is viewed from turns out to be very important; therefore, an interactive procedure for continuous real time rotation of the displayed object has been developed.

The author has heard of other versions of this type of device. In one case, a projection device is used to put a sequence of pictures on a one-foot square translucent screen that moves through a one-foot volume. The screen performs the same function as the vibrating mirror. Another variation uses an electromechanical modulator to unscramble the same type of continuously deformed display that is being put up on the high resolution CRT used with a vibrating mirror.

New developments may be made that will allow a full-color true 3D display device. This is like adding a fifth dimension to x, y, z, and motion. Given that mirrors can be used to overlay images, it seems feasible to put colored filters in front of different CRTs and merge the images to achieve a full-color 3D display. The phosphor persistence in color CRTs causes the image to streak in the Z-axis on a vibrating mirror. Therefore, a sufficiently fast phosphor needs to be filtered, or an aperature stop needs to be built that will cut off the image in the required time. The bottom line is that there is not a

(text continued on page 203.

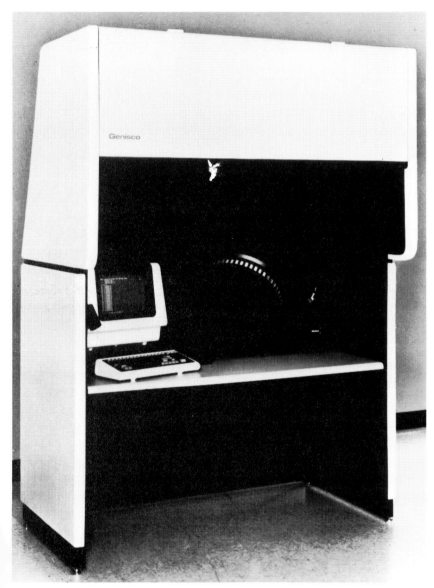

Figure 8-10. The Genisco SpaceGraph vibrating mirror 3D display device. A 40-cm vibrating mirror is partially shown at the center of the display. A high-resolution CRT is housed within the overhead casing. (Courtesy Hand Stover, Genisco Computer Corp.)

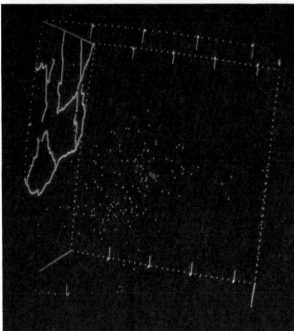

Figure 8-11. These photographs were taken from different viewing angles of a single display on the SpaceGraph. The photos represent earthquake epicenters under an active Japanese fault belt. The red dot appearing on the left-hand photo is an LED pointer that can be moved throughout the 3D image. While appearing 3D on the screen, any photographs taken from it appear two dimensional, as shown.

perfect 3D display device and a complete solution has yet to be developed.

Geophysical applications for true 3D display devices are very widespread, because almost all of the data and problems being evaluated are multi-dimensional. This, of course, starts with multi-dimensional information from the seismic trace. For example, Petty-Ray Geophysical Research has illustrated interesting visual evaluations of a three-component seismic trace.[35] Three views of a three component seismic trace at two different times are shown in Figures 8-12 and 8-13. This display is from an E & S color vector refresh graphics system. The light blue vector represents a 10-ms tracking window that can be moved through the trace to show 3D energy with time. This is only the beginning of evaluating the type of multi-dimensional problems facing explorationists.

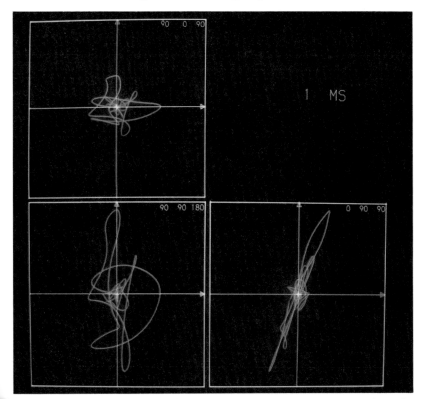

Figure 8-12. First of two views of a three-component seismic trace displayed with window partitioning. The large events in the lower right view are ground roll and airwave noise. Reflection events are hidden in the smaller amplitude clusters around the origin. (Courtesy Geosource, Petty-Ray Geophysical Division.)

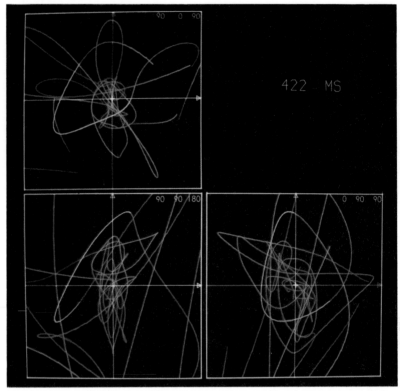

Figure 8-13. This is a larger scale display of Figure 8-12 with a 10 ms tracking window at 422 ms. The viewing directions may be rotated with analog dials. Also, the tracking window may be altered in length and in the rate of track. (Courtesy Geosource, Petty-Ray Geophysical Division.)

SUMMARY

An interactive, high-resolution 3D volume display device is needed to help evaluate the volumes of geological and geophysical data being generated today. Once there are "smoke-filled" rooms within which each voxel can be independently displayed, and users have hands-on evaluation of the data, many fields will reap the benefits of the technology. There have been 3D display developments in other scientific disciplines, even in the entertainment field, that may aid in the development of a workable 3D display system or technique for exploration; however, before geoscientists use true 3D display devices, effective methods must be developed for using high-resolution, two-dimensional computer graphics for interactive interpretation and processing. Experience developed in 2D can then be applied effectively to simultaneously evaluate an entire data volume on a 3D display device.

References

1. Nelson, H. R., Jr., "Interactive Graphics Enhances Seismic Data Display," *World Oil*, March, 1981, pp. 76-82.
2. Berkhout, A. J., "Acquisition and Processing Techniques in Medical Imaging," presentation given at the 51st annual international SEG meeting, Los Angeles, Calif., 1981. (See abstract, *Geophysics*, V. 47, No. 4, pp. 468, 1982.)
3. Harris, L. D., *et al*, "Display and Visualization of Three-Dimensional Reconstructed Anatomic Morphology: Experience with the Thorax, Heart, and Coronary Vasculature of Dogs," *Journal of Computer Assisted Tomography*, V. 3, No. 4, pp. 439-446, Aug., 1979.
4. Baxter, B., University of Utah Medical Center, Salt Lake City, Utah, personal communication, Sept., 1979.
5. Herman, G. T., "Detection and Display of Organ Surfaces from Computed Tomograms," presentation at IGC (The Institute for Graphic Communication) conference on Three-Dimensional Display Techniques, Andover, Mass., May 20-22, 1980.
6. Budinger, T. F., *et al*, "Transverse Section Imaging with Heavy Charged Particles: Theory and Applications," Image Processing for 2-D and 3-D Reconstruction from Projections: Theory and Practice in Medical and the Physical Sciences, digest of technical papers at topical meeting, Stanford University, Stanford, Calif., Aug. 4-7, 1975.
7. Langridge, R., *et al*, "Real-Time Color Graphics in Studies of Molecular Interacton," *Science*, V. 211, No. 4483, pp. 661-666.
8. Sobel, I., "Computer Aided Reconstruction by Tracing of Serial Sections (CARTOS)," presentation at IGC conference on Three-Dimensional Display Techniques, Andover, Mass., May 20-22, 1980.
9. Hasler, A. F., des Jardins, M., and Negri, A. J., "Artificial Stereo Presentations of Meteorological Data Fields," PREPRINT accepted by *Bulletin American Meteoroligical Society*, April 1981, 13 p.
10. Hasler, A. F., "Stereographic Observations from Geosynchronous Satellites: An Important New Tool for the Atmospheric Sciences," *Bulletin American Meteorological Society*, V. 62, No. 2, pp. 194-212, Feb. 1981.
11. McNally, K., "Geophysical Multi-Dimensional Data Display Problems and Future Potential," presentation at IGC conference on Three-Dimensional Display Techniques, Andover, Mass. May 20-22, 1980.
12. Simpson, A. L., "The Image Processing Gap," presentation by University of Houston Image Processing Laboratory to possible industry supporters, Houston, Tex., Oct. 1, 1981. (See also reprint, SAL Annual Progress Review, V. 8, pp. 528-535, 1981.)
13. Edelson, E., "The Bizarre New World of Holography," *Popular Science*, pp. 87-91, 168, March, 1979.
14. Ibid., p. 89.
15. Benton, S. A., "Evolution of Three-Dimensional Imaging Techniques," presentation at IGC conference on Three-Dimensional Display Techniques, Andover, Mass., May 20-22, 1980.

16. Simpson, A. L., "The Image Processing Lab: Status and Plans," presentation at the semi-annual meeting of the Seismic Acoustics Laboratory, University of Houston, Houston, Texas., May 7, 1981. (See reprint, SAL Annual Progress Review, V. 8, pp. 518-527, 1981.)

17. Hamblin, W. K., and Howard, J. D., Physical Geology Laboratory Manual, Burgess Publishing Co., 1967, p. 159.

18. Harris, L. D., Biodynamics Research Unit, Mayo Foundation, Rochester, Minnesota, personal communications, 1981.

19. Verm, R. W. and Simpson, A. L., "Motion as an Aid to the Perception of Three Dimensions," SAL Semi-Annual Progress Review, V. 7, pp. E1-19, 1981.

20. Harris, L. D., Robb. R. A., and Ritman, E. L., "Visual Enhancement and Display of Three-Dimensional Reconstruction Anatomic Morphology," *Sixth Computer Radiology*, pp. 278-284, June, 1979.

21. Nelson, H. R., Jr., "3D Seismic Techniques Aid Exploration, Development," *World Oil*, pp. 115-120, Dec., 1981.

22. Nelson, H. R., Jr. "Modeling Resolves Complex Seismic Events," *World Oil*, pp. 61-70, Feb., 1982.

23. Harris, L. D., and Nelson, H. R., Jr., "Three-Dimensional Display and Analysis of Seismic Volume Images," SEG Proceedings, V. 2, pp. 2037-2045, 1981 (see abstract, *Geophysics*, V. 47, No. 4, p. 468, 1982).

24. Chung, S. J. "Stereoscopic Imaging of Three-Dimensional Seismic Data," M.Sc. Thesis, University of Houston, Dec., 1981.

25. Butterfield, J. F., Autostereoscopic Film Display, SAL Semi-Annual Progress Review, V. 7, pp. F26-40, May, 1981.

26. de Montebello, R. L., "The Synthalayzer for Three-Dimensional Synthesis, and Analysis by Optical Dissection," Proceedings of SPIE, V. 120, pp. 184-191, Aug. 25-27, 1977.

27. Budinger, T. F., "Introduction to the Fundamental Science Problems," notes from presentation at IGC conference on Three-Dimensional Display Techniques, Carmel, Calif., May 31-June 2, 1982.

28. Ricks, D. E., "A New Interactive 3D Display Provides High Resolution Color Images," SAL Semi-Annual Progress Review, V. 7, pp. F41-48, May, 1981.

29. Pizer, S., University of North Carolina, Chapel Hill, N.C., personal communication, 1982.

30. Jansson, D. G., *et al*, "A Three-Dimensional Computer Display," SAL Semi-Annual Progress Review, V. 7, pp. F8-25, 1981.

31. Jansson, D. G. and Goodhue, J. T., "Medical Applications of a New 3D Display-System," Proceedings of the National Computer Graphics Assn., Baltimore, Maryland, June 1981.

32. Sher, L. D., "The SpaceGraph Display: Principles of Operation and Application," SAL Semi-Annual Progress Review, V. 5, pp. 212-224, May, 1980.

33. Johnson, S. and Baxter, B., "Utah 3-D 'Volume Viewer': A True Three-D Display for Graphics, Geophysical and Other Applications," SAL Semi-Annual Progress Review, V. 5, pp. 225-232, 1980.

34. SpaceGraph, Genisco Computers Corp. Pamphlet, 1981.

35. Walker, C. D. and Massell, W. F. "Geophysics and Digital Graphics." Notes from presentation at the regional SEG chapter school on Digital Graphics, New Orleans, LA, April 28, 1982.

CHAPTER 9

Interactive Interpretation

A widespread movement in the oil industry is underway to develop computer systems and methods that will assist explorationists in handling the volumes of data being worked with today. Independent consultants and some contractors are using new microcomputers to increase the amount of data that can be evaluated over a given time. Simultaneously, the major oil companies and larger geophysical contractors are putting together very large, complex and expensive systems that promise to open many new doors for geophysical interpreters. This chapter reviews the major recent developments in interactive interpretation techniques, of which the author is aware and can publish.

Computer-aided analysis of geophysical data is the logical direction being taken to efficiently handle the volumes of data being worked with today. When tied to new developments in computerized display devices,[1][2] this application of computer technology is particularly relevant to interactive interpretation methods. Geophysical interpretation has not evolved, however, at the same rate or to the same degree as instrumentation, processing or field acquisition over the last few decades.[3] Therefore, it is reasonable to predict that interactive interpretation techniques will see substantial change and development in the near future.

WHY COMPUTERIZE?

As more and more explorationists are beginning to demand 3D seismic surveys for evaluating complex geologic sequences,[4] it is

207

apparent that a large problem with such survey data is paper mass. The paper handling problem is enormous and requires new methods of storage, manipulation and display. Attending the Norwegian Petroleum Society's 3D seismic techniques conference in March 1982, the author was astounded at the number of geophysicists insisting on 3D surveys for their interpretation work. This, despite the fact that the paper handling problem was recognized.

The use of interactive computer graphics appears to be the best available solution to this problem. And, of course, as seismic display techniques are developed for such interpretation purposes, it follows that parallel applications will also arise. These developments will include displaying seismic data on a CRT (cathode ray tube) in the field or in processing centers for quality control, and interactive parameter selection.

Another reason interactive interpretation is becoming an obvious solution for seismic interpreters is that they spend too much of their time doing things like timing sections, posting maps, contouring maps, calculating isochrons, converting time maps to depth maps (isochron maps to isopach maps), migrating contour maps, calculating potential reservoir volumes, doing economic analyses, and in general, "number crunching." With the time shortage explorationists face, it is key that new computer technologies be applied to interpretation techniques to improve the quality and quantity of work accomplished per unit time.

COMPUTER APPLICATIONS

Microcomputer

This is one device that can help seismic interpreters use their time more effectively. Figure 9-1 shows three hardcopy examples of one company's use of a microcomputer for such time-saving purposes. This system hardware consists of a Z80-based microcomputer with two 1-Megabyte floppy disks, a black and white graphics CRT, a digitizing data tablet and a printer with graphics output capabilities. The system is being designed to handle the data on a "by prospect" basis and will allow entry of seismic lines, seismic horizons, faults, well logs, gravity or magnetic surveys, model parameters, and the like for a specific prospect.[5]

There are several geophysicists, including some independent consultants whom the author knows, who have brought small microcomputers themselves and have developed personal software packages to aid in different exploration number crunching operations. Given recent advancements in small computers, the ease of linking them to other computers (minicomputers or mainframes) and their lowered costs, a great increase in the number and sophistication of such systems is certain.

Explorationists will surely be using interpretation workstations in remote locations in the near future. For example, Landmark Graphics Corporation, Texas Instruments, GECO, and the Denver Processing Center are introducing interpretation workstations to the market place in 1983. The Landmark workstation will be built from a "family of products" in a modular manner. The system is planned to be based on the Intel 80286/80287 10 MHz C.P.U.[6] With a multi-bus main chassis, this "microcomputer" can have up to 16 megabytes of main RAM memory, array processors, an Ethernet communication network controller, up to eight 440-megabyte Winchester discs, 9-track tri-density tape drives, digitizers, hardcopy units, and a 1024 by 1024 6-byte pixel 2-overlay color display monitor.

Having such inexpensive number crunching aids will be of particular benefit to consulting interpreters. The microcomputer will provide an economic and logistic tool with the potential of greatly increasing productivity and accuracy. An example of the type of interpretation tools that will become more available is numerical modeling.[7] The ability to take an interpretation and generate critical synthetic traces or sections will provide consulting interpreters with a check on their work as well as support for client presentations. As areas are worked, the interpreter can build a digital information file about each specific prospect. This provides compact storage of key information like horizon picks, contour maps, well log information, etc. The computer forces an organized storage system if the files are to fulfill their planned and potential use.

A

FORMATION NAME	DEPTH	TIME	AVG. VELO.
MOWRY	617.	.01800	8222.22
MUDDY	805.	.06200	8451.61
SKULL CREEK	840.	.07025	8455.52
DAKOTA	1110.	.13556	8365.57
FUSON	1186.	.15060	8539.18
LAKOTA	1192.	.15180	8550.73
SUNDANCE	1485.	.20764	9073.55
SPEARFISH	1897.	.28900	9370.24
MINNEKAHTA	2576.	.38707	10504.65
OPECHE	2620.	.39189	10599.94
MINNELUSA	2672.	.39943	10660.23

B

ISOCHRON CONTOURS FOR HORIZONS 1–4
Z LOW = 629.000   Z HIGH = 733.000   SPACING 10.400

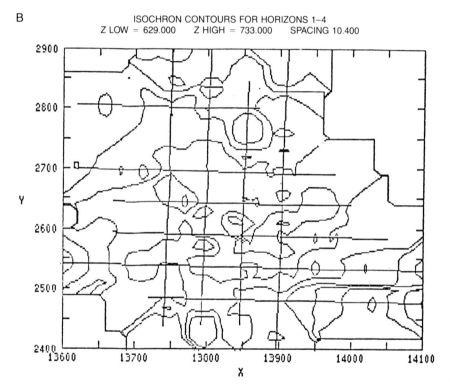

C

THICKNESS INCREASES FROM THE NORTHWEST TO THE SOUTHEAST

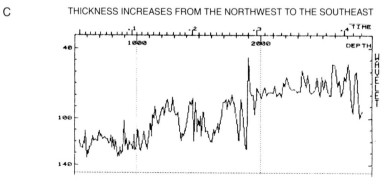

Minicomputer

As the complexity of interpretation problems increases, microcomputers must then be linked to larger minicomputers. The microcomputers can be used as an intelligent terminal that "talks" to the larger computers; however, these small home computers do not, in general, have computation power sufficient to perform complex operations like calculating a 2D forward model seismic section. Basic parameters defining the model can be entered over a phone line from any microcomputer with a modum, and then the results picked up from a supporting computer facility after the run is completed.

Applications

The use of any type of computer in resource evaluation is new and requires new skills and innovative applications to take advantage of the capabilities. Examples of the ways new computer power is being used in exploration were presented at the Tenth Geochautauqua on Computer Applications in the Earth Sciences in Ottawa, Canada (Oct. 23,-24, 1981).[8] One paper presented a statistical evaluation of oil and gas prospects in the Outer Continental Shelf of the Gulf Coast. For structurally controlled traps mapped by seismic techniques before drilling, John Davis (Kansas Geological Survey) and John Harbaugh (Stanford University) developed simple statistical relationships between the size, shape and other attributes of the traps and the presence and size of their petroleum and natural gas reservoirs. Predictions based on numerical regressions between seismic structural properties and reservoir volumes had significant correlation. These statistical techniques have obvious application as part of an interactive interpretation system.

Figure 9-1. Microcomputers can help seismic interpreters use their time more effectively. A shows a time/depth chart from a sonic log for eleven horizons in one prospect. The time of horizons at specific station numbers along the seismic line can also be listed. These values can be picked from a sonic log or a seismic section using a standard digitizing tablet. B shows how the map line locations can be overlain on merged horizon time maps to generate an initial isochron map. C shows a segment of a sonic log. This information can be converted to a synthetic seismic trace, scaled, and output in hardcopy form to tie to paper sections. (Courtesy C. E. Burton and S. Stockton, Professional Geophysics, Inc.)

Several basic design considerations for building an effective interactive interpretation system have been described by Robert Hodgson, President of Geoquest, et al.[9] First, it is reasonable to plan system development on an evolving basis with expansion capability. This development should include hardware, data bases, application and user training. Second, it is important that the systems be "user friendly." As graphics systems for interactive interpretation become more widespread, most of the users will not be computer experts, nor will they use a system unless it is simple, reliable, and solves specific number-crunching problems. Third, the system must address interface design. This means that existing capabilities, like data procedures, should be integrated into the new system. Fourth, these systems should accommodate different levels of user expertise. This allows a technician to generate accurate exploration base maps, or an experienced geophysicist to do theoretical modeling, on the same system. The system that allows all of these options will have more capacity than the standard available microcomputer, and would be more closely related to a small minicomputer.

Computer mapping systems have already developed to the point where they are becoming the basis for another type of interactive interpretation system. A key problem in using any system for this purpose is to accurately register and merge the different base maps that will be used. There are several mapping systems available that have effectively solved this. For example, a base map can be placed on up to a 44 in. by 60 in. (111 cm by 152 cm) digitizing tablet, and then each point on the map can be digitized with an accuracy of 0.01 in. (0.25 mm).[10] The key to any of these systems is building a file of information that can be recalled to aid in interpretation. The same input procedures can be used for well locations, directional drilling data, leases, formation tops, seismic sections (at least a line drawing representation of key horizon picks), well logs, production data, and legal property information such as lease description, land owner, lease holder, lease expiration date and other pertinent · information.

One system, the Integraph system, allows access to the exploration data base in graphical form, tabular form, or both.[11] The data processing hardware of some of these mapping systems is based around Digital Equipment Corp. processors, like a PDP-1134 or a VAX. Several major contractors have geophysical processing packages built around this same type of equipment. As these system capabilities are merged, they become tools capable of helping with interactive geophysical analysis.

INTERACTIVE INTERPRETATION

In order for seismic interpreters to effectively take advantage of computer number-crunching capabilities, the data that will be interpreted needs to be digitally stored and displayed.[1] Once this is accomplished, it is possible to follow the eight generalized steps of doing interactive interpretation as described in Figure 9-2.[3]

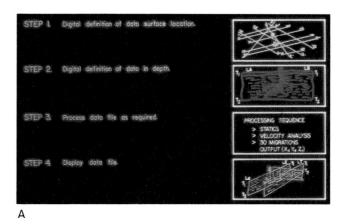

A

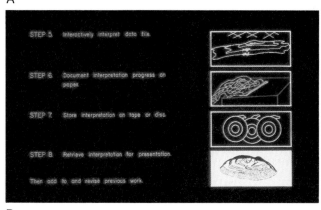

B

Figure 9-2. Eight generalized steps for doing interactive interpretation. (Courtesy SEG.)

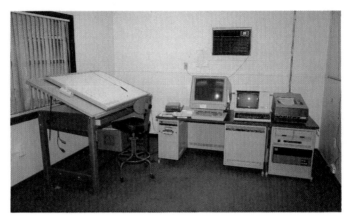

Figure 9-3. Typical example of the type of "intelligent" terminals, available in most oil companies, that can be modified to be an interactive interpretation console. This system consists of a Tektronix 4081, tied to a large digitizing tablet, a hardcopy unit and a VAX minicomputer. The CRT on the right is a standard VT-100 Digital Equipment Corp. user terminal that has been modified for color and vector display (resolution 512 by 480 pixels). (Courtesy University of Houston Research Computation Lab.)

The basic hardware to accomplish these operations presently exists in most oil companies. Figure 9-3 shows this kind of basic system. With a useable software package, this system can be used to save an interpreter hours of needless number crunching.

With a relatively inexpensive hardware modification, standard VT 100 programming terminal can be converted to include color and vector display capabilities. The smaller CRT unit shown in Figure 9-3 (costing about $2,000) has been modified with a graphics package and for color display of eight colors (another $4,000). Figure 9-4 shows examples of vertical seismic sections being displayed on this device with the eight colors being a function of reflection amplitude. These sections are from a complex physical model, called SALNOR, built by the University of Houston's Seismic Acoustics Laboratory (SAL) for Statoil of Norway. The sections represent a typical North Sea geologic sequence. An unprocessed section and a 3D migrated section are shown for comparison. One problem with this particular display is that it is not interactive. In this case the VT-100 is connected to a VAX system via a 9,600 baud line. It takes 15 minutes to build a single picture at this data transfer rate.

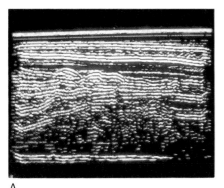
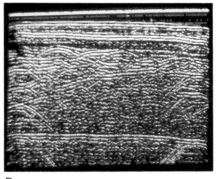

A   B

Figure 9-4. The seismic sections shown are displayed on a modified VT-100 terminal. The first illustration is of an unprocessed section and the second is a 3D migrated version of the same data (there is a scale difference in the two sections). The eight colors are assigned to each pixel as a function of the amplitude of the seismic trace. The data is from a model built to represent a typical North Sea geologic sequence.

INTELLIGENT PICTURE PROCESSORS

Vector Refresh Graphics

If there is a direct memory access (DMA) link between a picture processor and a supporting computer, the display of data sets can occur rapidly enough to be considered interactive. One example of this is a project done at the Image Processing Laboratory (IPL) on the Adage Vector Refresh Graphics system.[12] The sequence shown in Figure 9-5 illustrates how this system has been used for interactive 3D interpretation.

In this example, a simple single-surface structural model, called SALGLF, is interpreted. After the best parameters are chosen for data display, a set of parallel seismic sections are reformatted for display. This allows the data to be dislayed on a CRT screen using the Adage raster segment generator (RSG). These seismic sections can be shown on the screen one after another in the time it takes to push a function button (if the multi-processing central processing unit is not being taxed). This allows the interpreter to move rapidly through a data set and obtain a general feel for structural attitudes.

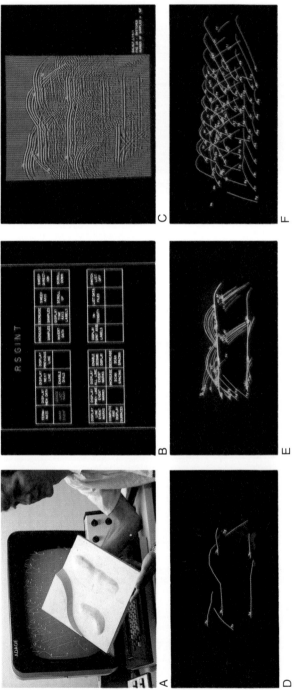

Figure 9-5. This sequence of photos illustrates the steps taken in interpreting seismic data using an Adage Raster Segment Generator. The 12 sq. in. (scaled 12,000 sq. ft.) physical model the seismic data was taken from is shown by Richard Verm in A. The function buttons assignments shown in B illustrate the procedures that can be chosen for interactive interpretation of the data. C shows one vertical seismic slice taken across the model, while D illustrates the interpreter's picks from that data. E is the compilation of picks from 10 different vertical seismic sections across the model and G is the rotation of the same data. (Courtesy SEG.[12])

Utilizing the graphics screen is quite simple. The assigned roles of the 16 function buttons are available on the screen at the push of a switch. When the user is ready, the proper function button is chosen and enabled (activated), and the events are thereby displayed on the screen. The user can then choose, "pick" or mark the areas of interest from each display by using a standard digitized tablet and a linked screen cursor. This is the interpretation stage.

After one display is interpreted, the next parallel section is displayed and interpreted, with the previous interpretation also being displayed for reference, if needed. At any time, the user can disable the seismic section being displayed and look only at the interpretation of a single line, or at all of the interpretations from previously displayed sections.

During this entire process, the user/interpreter has the option to rotate the interpretation being displayed. The motion parallax that accompanies the rotational movement of the interpretation makes it appear 3D to viewers.[2] The result is that a 3D interpretation is accomplished interactively in a relatively short time.

Illustrating the time-saving ability of such interactive processes is simple. Consider that a more complex single-surface model than the one used in the foregoing illustration has been used for several years by Fred Hilterman in an SEG workshop titled "3D Seismic Techniques."[13] In attempting to interpret the seismic sections taken over this model, which includes complex faulting, teams of experienced interpreters have needed up to six hours for completion. Using the Adage interactive interpretation program, a visually understandable interpretation of this same data set has been built in about 30 minutes.

Field data also can be readily interpreted using this same display equipment. The sequence of seismic sections shown in Figure 9-6 illustrates the zooming in on a chosen portion of a larger seismic section. This example is from the Wind River Basin overthrust area.[14] The resolution is certainly good enough for an interpretation to be done using the same procedures described for interpreting the physical model data in the preceding paragraphs.

Note that the Figure 9-6 displays are black and white only; yet, there is as much information as is normally used for an interpretation. Using color, however, will provide an entirely new dimension. If it is added properly, color will allow a visual interpretation of the spectral analysis of the data. That is, data can be displayed as

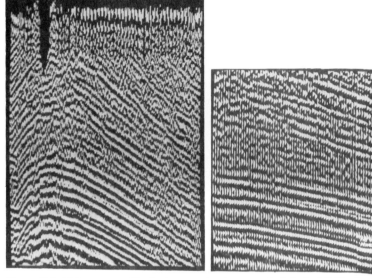

Figure 9-6. *This sequence illustrates zooming in on a set of stacked field seismic sections from the Wyoming Wind River basin. Using an Adage Raster Segment Generator (RSG), the first section is displayed at 1-bit resolution (each sample is either off for negative polarity or on for positive). This allows 1,000 samples to be displayed on 240 traces without flicker. The last section, an enlarged portion from the first, is displayed at 2-bit resolution (each sample can be off, on with 1 unit length or on with 2 units length). This allows 1,000 samples to be displayed on 120 traces without flicker for a single display.[14]*

a function of varying seismic attributes such as amplitude, instantaneous phase or frequency, apparent polarity, velocity, etc.[15,16,17]

The successful use of color for interactive display has been shown by Geosource. This company is using an Evans & Sutherland color vector graphics system to display similar interpretations from data collected from offshore through the use of a marine cross-dip survey.[17] The sequence of data shown in Figures 9-7 and 7-4 is the displayed result of this survey.

As Figure 9-7 illustrates, the data consists of sets of parallel lines that are collected from two sources, offset from either side of a ship by paravanes. These sources alternate shooting into a single cable.[18] The two lines that are collected have a subsurface separation of about 100 m. After the data is processed, each pair of lines is interpreted on the CRT screen in order to obtain the cross-dip component, as illustrated in Figure 9-7A.

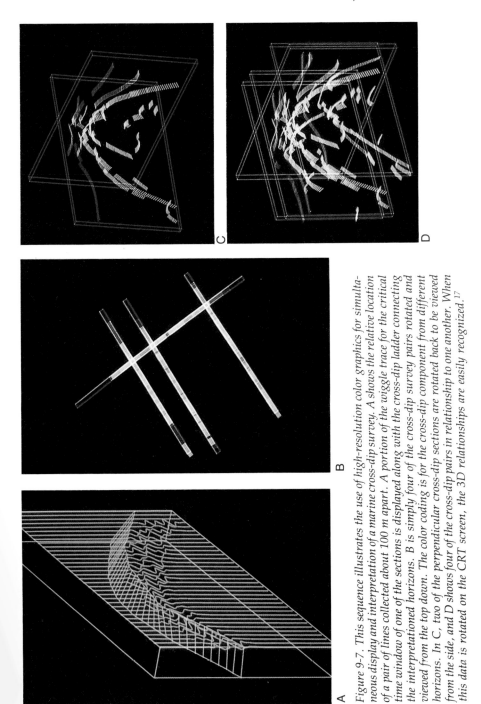

Figure 9-7. This sequence illustrates the use of high-resolution color graphics for simultaneous display and interpretation of a marine cross-dip survey. A shows the relative location of a pair of lines collected about 100 m apart. A portion of the wiggle trace for the critical time window of one of the sections is displayed along with the cross-dip ladder connecting the interpretationed horizons. B is simply four of the cross-dip survey pairs rotated and viewed from the top down. The color coding is for the cross-dip component from different horizons. In C, two of the perpendicular cross-dip sections are rotated back to be viewed from the side, and D shows four of the cross-dip pairs in relationship to one another. When this data is rotated on the CRT screen, the 3D relationships are easily recognized.[17]

The entire four-line cross-dip survey is displayed in Figure 9-7B, only in map view (from the top down). Each of the four seismic lines shown is really a pair of sections. In this case, where 48 miles of Gulf of Mexico cross-dip data is seen, the map geometry is maintained, but the separation of the parallel lines is exaggerated. The cross-dip component from different horizons is color coded to match from line to line.

A portion of the same data set is again shown Figure 9-7C. However, only the two perpendicular line pairs chosen have been rotated in order to evaluate the structure. And in Figure 9-7D, the picked cross-dip components on all four line pairs are displayed. Although it is confusing in the still picture, when the data is rotated the 3D relationships are easily recognized.

Color Raster Graphics

While vector refresh graphics is workable for interactive interpretation, there presently appears to be more widespread use of color raster graphics in the oil industry. This is primarily due to the ability to display more data at a much lower cost. Figure 9-4 shows there is enough resolution on even a 512 by 480 raster scope to view sufficient data for an interactive evaluation. And this viewing capacity is further enhanced when working with data volumes from 3D seismic surveys.[4]

As Figure 9-8 illustrates, an increased area can be viewed by displaying horizontal rather than vertical sections on a CRT. The reason is that the spatial sampling is much larger than the temporal sampling. This example was calculated based on a 1981 vector refresh graphics limitation of 21,500 vectors.[3] Each vertical section had 86 traces with 250 samples each. With a velocity of 7,000 fps (2,134 mps) and 150-ft trace spacing (45 m), the vertical display showed less than one-tenth the area the horizontal section display did for the same number of vectors. This same vertical/horizontal display ratio was maintained when the number of displayable 2D vectors was increased to 90,000, or when a 1024 by 1024 raster display device was used.

Phillips Petroleum provided a 3D seismic volume to several raster graphics vendors for use as a benchmark in 1982. Some of these horizontal section displays have been released for public showing by the vendors. Figure 9-9 illustrates the resolution that

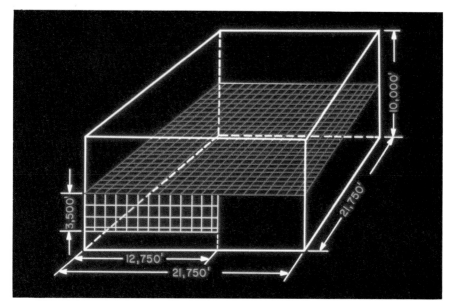

Figure 9-8. This graph illustrates the relative subsurface area that can be displayed using the same number of pixels for a horizontal versus a vertical seismic section. The difference is due to the difference in temporal and spatial sampling.[3]

can be obtained in displaying a horizontal time section on a high resolution raster CRT. An interpretation can be accomplished from this data in the same way that it is using G.S.I.'s Seiscrop Interpretation Table.[19] In fact, when these horizontal time slices are animated fast enough on a raster graphics system, they replace the currently commonplace "movie presentations" of horizontal sections. This type of animation has been accomplished on the Adage system, the CDC Ramtek, and several other advanced graphics systems. For true animation, each new seismic section is being displayed in less than one-tenth a second.[12] If raster CRTs are configured correctly they can exceed this refresh rate.

Figure 9-10 is a series of slides of the same Phillip's data set, displayed on an Ikonas graphics system. From this series of examples it is apparent how this type of display device can allow interactive interpretation. Phillips provided 39 times slices that were sequenced through forward and backwards at variable speeds. Note that four time slices are shown, labeled 22, 23, 24, and 25. Figure 9-10C shows pseudocontouring, whereby a range of amplitude

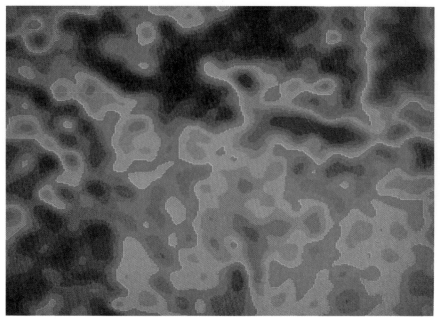

Figure 9-9. Note that the resolution possible on this display of a horizontal seismic section on a high resolution raster scope is quite adequate for interpretation. (Courtesy Phillips Petroleum and Ramtek.)

levels are blacked out. With specific amplitude ranges blacked out the data set can still be sequenced through. Figures 9-10D, E , and F show how the relationship of the color in reference to the amplitude values can be changed through color map animation. Figure 9-10G illustrates annotated contouring that was saved from the time slice as shown in Figure 9-10B. Again, this series of examples shows how this type of display device could allow interactive interpretation, when new data is displayed rapidly enough.

True Image Processing Systems

These add yet another dimension to an interactive processing system. With a digital image and a pipeline processor, there are numerous ways a data set can be manipulated and certain characteristics enhanced in real time. This is impossible to accomplish when the data being worked with are stored on a film medium. Some of the basic manipulations include image addition, subtraction, multiplication, scaling and look-up type corrections.

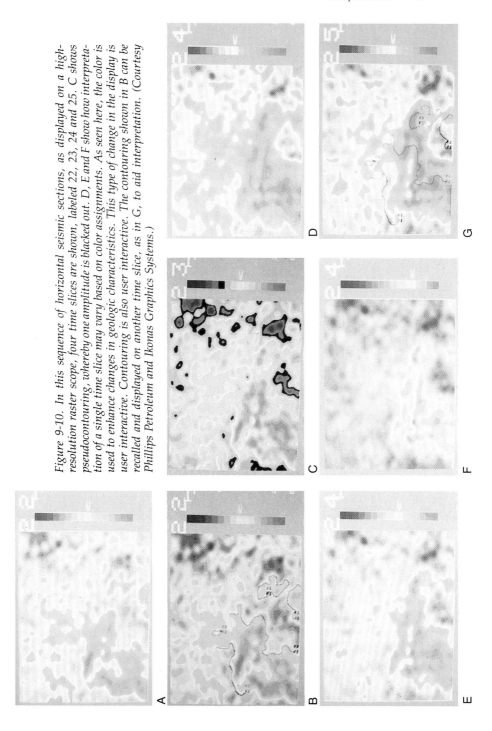

Figure 9-10. In this sequence of horizontal seismic sections, as displayed on a high-resolution raster scope, four time slices are shown, labeled 22, 23, 24 and 25. C shows pseudocontouring, whereby one amplitude is blacked out. D, E and F show how interpretation of a single time slice may vary based on color assignments. As seen here, the color is used to enhance changes in geologic characteristics. This type of change in the display is user interactive. Contouring is also user interactive. The contouring shown in B can be recalled and displayed on another time slice, as in G, to aid interpretation. (Courtesy Phillips Petroleum and Ikonas Graphics Systems.)

These operations can be accomplished in a one-frame time period on many image processing systems.[20] More advanced operations include digital filtering, matrix multiplication, statistics, vector dot products, image merging (weighted sums) and edge operations.[21] The interactive interpretation systems that will find general use within a few years will allow overlaying of different types of sections (raw, filtered, migrated, synthetic, etc.), gravity, magnetics, landsat and well log information, among others. Imagine the assistance to an interpreter of interactively picking a section, calculating a synthetic section from the interpretation, and overlaying or subtracting the synthetic from the original data to see where there are problems with the interpretation.

Of course, while manipulation of softcopy is desirable, it is important that a hardcopy also can be made of critical steps in the CRT softcopy interpretation. Prakla Seismos produced some interesting soft- and hardcopy seismic displays using a system called Uniras. The seismic section is first previewed on a Lexidata color CRT and then plotted on an Applicon Ink Jet Plotter.[22] A simpler hardcopy procedure seems to be to take a picture. There are Polaroid 8 in. by 10 in. systems available, and if the time necessary for slide processing is not critical, then any good 35 mm camera will do. One of the best hardcopy procedures is to dump the display images through the CRT video bus to a video recorder. This provides storage of animation sequences, as well as what happened during an image processing session like filtering, matrix multiplication or image overlaying.

INDUSTRY PRESENTATIONS

Largely due to competition within the seismic industry, public presentations that display how computer graphics can be used as an aid to interactive interpretation have been generalized and vague. However, one of the best presentations the author has seen was made by Conoco Oil Co. personnel at the 1981 SEG convention in Los Angeles, California.[23] In this presentation it was illustrated that each lithological unit boundary can be distinguished by a unique color pattern, where color is used to illustrate simultaneous changes in all seismic variables. Instant, on-the-spot enhancements are possible for the interpreter. The system is described as an interactive color video display, and is based on hardware from International Imaging Systems. This technology is especially useful in working with 3D data volumes. A movie was presented showing how an interpreter would move through typical vertical sections or horizontal time-slice displays from a cube of 3D data. The examples included showed how these techniques apply to both bright spot and 3D data sets.

The display of 3D data volumes using interactive graphics has also been done by Chevron.[24] Their system is based on a Grinnel graphics system tied to a dedicated VAX. They can put a new frame on the screen every 12 seconds. When the speed is increased a hundred times for a movie presentation, an effective display for 3D seismic data evaluation results.

Two examples of Chevron's work were shown in Norway. The first involved data from the symmetric SALGLF model. Beginning the presentation, a sequence of vertical sections was marched through along both the x and y axes. Then the movement was repeated for a sequence of horizontal sections moved up and down the z axes. Next, a cube was outlined on the screen, and the visible faces filled with the appropriate seismic sections. The horizontal and vertical sections were again stepped through, only this time they appeared to be within the cube outline that remained displayed. The last sequence was to display a sweep of vertical sections from one edge to an adjacent edge of the cube. This started with a section along the y axis, for example, and ended with an x axis section. This same procedure was repeated with a 3D field survey over the East Painter field in the Wyoming Overthrust belt.

APPROACHING DEVELOPMENTS

As software development proceeds in time, interactive interpretation capabilities will be enhanced correspondingly. A problem with displaying 3D seismic data volumes has been correlating vertical sections to the appropriate horizontal time slice, or to tie two perpendicular vertical sections to one another. Traditionally, the only way this has been done effectively is through the bending, folding and manipulation of hardcopies of the sections in question. The effectiveness of doing this type of display splicing on the CRT has been shown using physical model data.[25][26] This is of great benefit to the interpreter in the evaluation of complex 3D relationships.

Also in the development stage is a display system that will enable large displays (40 in. by 40 in.) with 3 mil line width and no flicker. The system will have a maximum of four colors, with vector or raster scanning capability. The project, being undertaken by The Denver Processing Center is still labeled research (1983).[27] It is based on a liquid crystal display device similar to one being used by the military. A projection version of the system will be based on a laser driven liquid crystal, which will allow very large displays with high resolution.

An approximation to such large screen display can also be achieved with present commercial devices by designing the software to move the display window through the data volume. If an overview of a larger data set is needed then a zoom-out capability would have to be incorporated. This requires that all of the data be in a direct access, extended picture memory.

As devices with this capability are developed, there will be other applications found. For example, if there is enough memory to store a complete raw 3D data volume, it is reasonable to think of doing a 3D migration of that data without having to page later from different migration aperture locations in and out of memory. Other applications of such memory capability include subjects like pattern recognition, artificial intelligence and automatic computer interpretation.

The critical benefit from these enhancements in speed, size and flexibility of display will be improvements in the quality of interpretation. Interactive access to other geologic/geophysical data sets will allow seismic interpreters to build a better geologic interpretation of the subsurface. Data that will be incorporated includes gravity, magnetics, geochemical, well log, and others.

Interpreters also will come to understand subtle characteristics of and problems with the seismic data when they have tools that allow a detailed and rapid analysis with many options. For illustration, consider the sequence of pictures in Figure 9-11 provided by Wulf

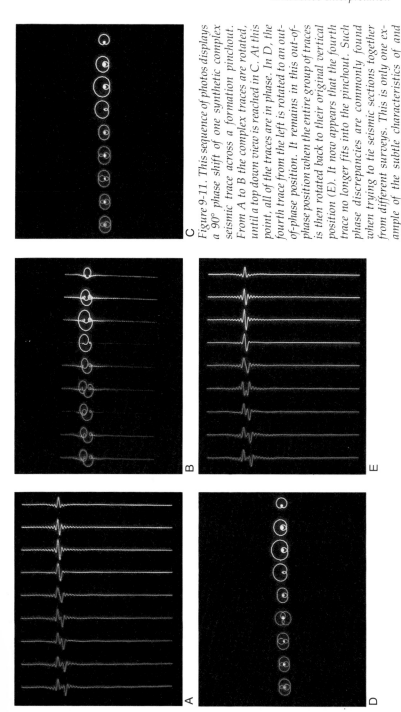

Figure 9-11. This sequence of photos displays a 90° phase shift of one synthetic complex seismic trace across a formation pinchout. From A to B the complex traces are rotated, until a top down view is reached in C. At this point, all of the traces are in phase. In D, the fourth trace from the left is rotated to an out-of-phase position. It remains in this out-of-phase position when the entire group of traces is then rotated back to their original vertical position (E). It now appears that the fourth trace no longer fits into the pinchout. Such phase discrepancies are commonly found when trying to tie seismic sections together from different surveys. This is only one example of the subtle characteristics of and problems with seismic data interpretation. (Courtesy Geosource, Petty-Ray Geophysical Division.)

Massell, director of research at Geosource Petty-Ray Research.[17] In this example, complex synthetic traces across a pinchout are displayed. Note the tuning effect in Figure 9-11A (the colors are only used to keep track of different traces). When these traces are rotated (Figure 9-11B) and looked directly down upon (Figure 9-11C), they are all in phase. However, notice that the fourth trace from the left (red) is rotated 90 degrees out of phase (Figure 9-11D) before the entire sequence is rotated back to its original position, as illustrated in Figure 9-11E. The fourth trace in Figure 9-11F no longer seems to fit into the pinchout. Such a phase shift is commonly found when tying sections together from different seismic surveys. Of course, there are numerous similar data problems that are not obvious on standard sections, or else not solvable within the time frame available for detailed analysis by interpreters using present techniques. Interactive techniques will allow such subtle characteristics of seismic data to be evaluated.

SUMMARY

Interactive interpretation techniques have come of age for the explorationist. They are desperately needed to handle the volumes of data being worked with today, particularly data from 3D seismic surveys. Many different kinds of systems are either in use or under development to meet these needs. This trend towards increased research in the field of interactive interpretation has been underway among major oil companies and contractors for several years now, and it is reasonable to project that development of this technology during this decade will be more rapid than that of most other new technologies in exploration geophysics. Just as children have left their televisions for video arcades, explorationists will soon replace their colored pencils with a computer graphics workstation.

References

1. Nelson, H. R., Jr., "Interactive Graphics Enhance Seismic Data Display," *World Oil*, pp. 76-82, Mar. 1982.
2. Nelson, H. R., Jr., "Will True 3D Display Devices Aid Geologic Interpretation?," *World Oil*, pp. 129-136, Apr. 1982.

3. Nelson, H. R., Jr., Hilterman, F. J., and Gardner, G. H. F., "Introduction to Interactive 3D Interpretation," *Oil and Gas Journal*, V. 79, No. 40, pp. 106-125, 1981.

4. Nelson, H. R., Jr., "3D Seismic Techniques Aid Exploration, Development," *World Oil*, pp. 115-120, Dec. 1981.

5. Burton, C. E., Professional Geophysics Inc., Denver, Colorado, personal communication, 1982.

6. Mouton, J. O., Landmark Graphics Corporation, Houston, Texas, personal communication, 1982.

7. Nelson, H. R., Jr., "Modeling Resolves Complex Seismic Events," *World Oil*, pp. 61-70, Feb. 1, 1982.

8. McCammon, R. B. and Agterberg, F. P., "Computers Seeking Minerals," *Geotimes*, pp. 14-16, Jan. 1982.

9. Hodgson, R. N., *et al*, "Online Graphic Systems Speed Exploratory Analysis," *World Oil*, pp. 37-48, Feb. 15, 1982.

10. Here's the Simplest Way to Analyze Your Petroleum Data, Computer Research Corp. brochure, 1981.

11. Product Summary, Intergraph brochure, 1981.

12. Nelson, H. R., Jr., Gardner, T. N., and Hilterman, F. J., "Interpretation of Physical Model Tank Data with the Raster Segment Generator," SEG Technical Papers, V. 6, pp. 3619-3634, Los Angeles, 1981 (See abstract, *Geophysics*, V. 47, No. 4, pp. 497-498, 1982.)

13. Hilterman, F. J., and Morgan, T., "Interpretation Workshop Problem," SEG 3D Seismic Techniques School Notes, Section 4, Houston, 1981.

14. Nelson, H. R., Jr., Gardner, T. N., and Verm, R. W., "Interactively Displaying Data from a Disc Full of Seismic Traces," EAEG Convention, Cannes, France, Substitute paper, 1982 (See also SAL Annual Progress Review, V. 8, 1982).

15. Taner, M. T., Koehler, F., Sheriff, R. E., "Complex Seismic Trace Analysis," *Geophysics*, V. 44, No. 6, pp. 1041-1063, 1979.

16. McDonald, J. A., Gardner, G. H. F., and Kotcher, J. S., "Areal Seismic Methods for Determining the Extent of Acoustic Discontinuities," *Geophysics*, V. 46, No. 1, pp. 2-16, 1981.

17. Massell, W. F., Winningham, D. J., and Nelson, H. R., Jr., "Interactive Geophysical Analysis with 3D Color Graphics," SEG Convention, Los Angeles, paper 7.4, 1981 (See abstract, *Geophysics*, V. 47, No. 4, p. 468, 1982.)

18. Whittlesey, J. R. B., and Neidell, N. S., "Marine Cross-Dip Seismic Surveys—Three-Dimensional Recording and Mapping," OTC preprint, paper No. 3847, 1980.

19. Brown, A. R., "3D Seismic Interpretation Methods," preprint of presentation given at the SEG convention, San Francisco, 1978 (see also abstract, *Geophysics*, V. 44, No. 3, p. 383, 1979).

20. RDS-3000 Image Memory and Video Control, Ikonas Graphics Systems brochure, 1980.

21. Outline of Digital Video Processor Specifications, De Anza Systems brochure, 1981.

22. Seispak, A Uniras Product, European Software Contractors brochure, 1981.

23. Rice, G. W., Stebens, B. B., and Hall, P. M., "Interactive Color Display and Analysis—An Added Dimension to Seismic Interpretation," SEG Convention, Los Angeles, paper S7.5, 1981 (see abstract, *Geophysics,* V. 47, No. 4, p. 469, 1982.)

24. Peters, D.C., "Graphic Display of 3D Seismic Data," presentation at Norwegian Petroleum Society's Conference on 3-D Seismic Techniques, Kristiansand S., Norway, March 8-10, 1982.

25. Verm, R. W., and Nelson, H. R., Jr., "Interacively Mixing the Display of Horizontal and Vertical Sections," SAL Semi-Annual Progress Review, V. 9, pp. 409-422, 1982.

26. Fisher, D. A., Nelson, H. R., Jr., and Verm, R. W., "Interactive Display and Interpretation of a Complex Physical Model After 3D Migration," SAL Semi-Annual Progress Review, V. 9, pp. 423-448, 1982.

27. Tegland, E. R., "3D Seismic Methods, Turnaround Time and What the Future Holds," presentation at Norwegian Petroleum Society's Conference on 3D Seismic Tehniques, Kristiansand S., Norway, March 8-10, 1982.

CHAPTER 10

Managed Data Bases

Computers and digital data storage techniques potentially provide geo-physical and geological interpreters access to vast quantities of exploration information. This data access and handling is commonly referred to as data base management. Most data base handling procedures implemented to date have been less than successful in exploration organizations. This chapter discusses recent developments in data base management and satellite communication as they relate to exploration geophysics.

As the volumes of data available to explorationists increase, it is imperative that an efficient system for storing and accessing such data be developed. While on the surface this seems a very simplistic statement requiring a rather simplistic solution, at closer examination the task is a tremendous one. There is no ideal data base that will perfectly suit all of the varying disciplines within exploration.

The science that has been developed to address this task is called data base management (DBM). This chapter addresses some of the computerized approaches to data storage and retrieval currently being utilized or experimented with and then discusses a long-range application for such sophisticated data handling within the exploration industry, including optical disc storage and the use of satellite communications for data transmission.

WHY DBM?

It seems some people in the industry—specifically managers—are having a hard time being sold on the necessity for computerized data base management. However, if one has ever been a seismic interpreter, the problems associated with handling exploration data are readily evident. These are best illustrated by specific examples.

As a seismic interpreter, the author found that on a majority of interpretation assignments organizing and getting access to the right data sets in the proper format consumed up to half of the total project time. This generalization held fairly consistent for projects done for U.S. divisions, international affiliates, or on in-house generated projects over a five-year period.

A particularly frustrating example was an assignment given the author in 1975 to do a regional interpretation offshore Argentina. An earlier trade had provided 5,000 km of seismic data that had never been evaluated. However, the data could not be found anywhere. No one was sure where it was stored, and a thorough search of several warehouses did not turn it up. Therefore, a request was made for another copy of the data. The week the copied data set finally arrived, a draftsman remembered something about the original data set. It turned up in two map tubes, in the center of the top shelf of some very long bookshelves in one of the warehouses. The excuse for having missed it on the original search was that it was arbitrarily mixed with data from the Far East and every tube had not been emptied in the search. The point is that retrieval based on an individual's memory will not compare to retrieval based on computer memory, especialy with high personnel turnover rates. Similar problems occurred on most projects the author has been involved with simply because the filing systems were inscrutable.

Such examples point to the fact that the use of digitally stored data bases is important to the entire spectrum of corporate organizational philosophies within exploration. This ranges from the huge multinationals centralized around a large mainframe computer, to smaller companies with computer processing distributed among a network of mini-computers, to independent consultants that use commmercial data bases, like the Petroleum Information (P.I.) well log files.

Why Current Problems?

There are many reasons why current data base management systems used within the exploration industry are poorly designed and hence cause serious problems. A major factor is that data organizations has often been left to the most competent available geophysical technician, who normally has no training or experience in library management or data storage. Another factor is that the increase in exploration activity has created a shortage of qualified interpreters, and economic pressures give precedence to short-term objectives. With the rapid expansion of exploration over the last decade, most organizations have not put time into planning and implementing a workable DBM system. Therefore, the decision makers have not been convinced, based on systems implemented to date, that data base management will save time and money in the long run. Ironically, however, managerial initiative and long-term planning are the first steps to solving the problem.

Illustrating the problem of management commitment to DBM, Townsend described,[1] not completely in jest, seven steps that have been followed in the development of corporate data bases. These are:

1. Uncritical acceptance
2. Wild enthusiasm
3. Dejected disillusionment
4. Total confusion
5. Search for the guilty
6. Punishment of the innocent
7. Promotion of the nonparticipants

To this could be added:

8. Cautious pursuit of an organized data base system by new hirees trained in computer capabilities and unaware of corporate politics.

Many persons in this last category are now getting some management responsibility. Their implementation of workable DBM systems promises to have a major impact on future exploration procedures and results.

THE FOUNDATION OF DBM

Efficient data base management for the exploration industry requires the selection of appropriate computer hardware, software and display equipment. However, the foundation for such a system is the scheme or format chosen for data storage. It is imperative that portions of the data base be retrievable from a variety of avenues. That is, the computer must be able to rapidly access and output any type or classification of data requested from a given data base. Both the size of the data base and the access issues must be addressed when choosing an appropriate format.

Size of Data Base

When one reviews the many different data sets that need to be accessed by explorationists, the size of the computer's reference task comes to focus. These data sets include, among others: maps showing data location, geography, political boundaries, culture, lease information; maps from previous evaluations (seismic time maps, depth maps, isochron or isopach maps); location and navigation information; well log data; seismic velocity data; gravity and magnetic surveys; landsat imagery; aerial photography; side scanning radar plots; geochemical information; geological outcrop information; reports and textual material; or the seismic data at each processing step. Obviously, accessing all these data using any technique can be a problem.

Access

Even if there is only one type of data on file, data access can be a problem. For example, the Seismic Acoustics Laboratory at the University of Houston has six catalogs of seismic data and the related collection of location maps[2] defining over 1.5 million seismic traces or over 41 gigabytes (10^9) of data. For the first five years of the project, there was not a well-defined way to easily access a specific subset of these data. An organized system for managing the data base was implemented in late 1982. Under this DBM system, new data will be systematically added and the old data easily retrievable. This is a very small problem compared to the data oil companies must keep track of. However, it was very difficult to initiate the DBM system.

Ready access to the required data sets is, in general, not being provided to interpreters attempting to solve interpretation problems. Few, if any, interpreters can sit down at an interpretation work station, call up needed data sets and then use the computer interactively to aid in building an interpretation. In fact, few divisions within the same company are able to effectively transfer data sets for joint projects. This does not have to be the case; the technology is available.

STRUCTURING STORAGE

Successful implementation of a data base management system requires well-defined procedures for inputting data into a data base and efficient methods for retrieving, analyzing and interpreting these digital files. The system needs to be evolutionary along user-defined routes rather than being instantly created in a rigid format.[13] Because data bases are never static for long, such flexibility is critical. And yet, there must be some sort of structure that ties the data base together.

This structure can be critical to data retrieval when a data base becomes large, as they have a habit of doing. Even hands-on evaluation of a system gives the user virtually no information on how well the data base manager will perform when the system reaches maturity. As is generally the case in the "real world," there is not a "best" data base structure that works efficiently for all types of data bases and user requests.

Retrieval speed is a function of the system response time or the quantity of data base inquiry. Retrieval from an unstructured data set is a function of the size of the data set. Structuring a data set can reduce search time by a factor of 40,000.[4] Hierarchical or tree structures are widely used in data base management. For example, when geographic locations are kept at the first level of a hierarchical organization, an explorationist can rapidly "zoom" in on a particular area (subset) of interest.

Tree structured searches are like following the line of responsibility on a corporate organization chart. For example, suppose a data base were established for the world, and an interpreter wanted to look up the data in a specific lease block offshore Texas. The computer would search down the North America "branch," then the Texas "branch," then the offshore "branch" and end up with

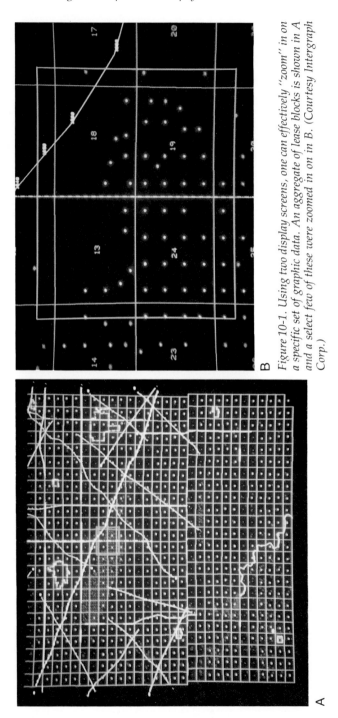

Figure 10-1. Using two display screens, one can effectively "zoom" in on a specific set of graphic data. An aggregate of lease blocks is shown in A and a select few of these were zoomed in on in B. (Courtesy Intergraph Corp.)

the lease block numbers requested. Each time a new "branch" in the "tree" is passed, all data in the data base not in that subset are ignored for the remainder of the search. Figure 10-1 illustrates the last two steps of this type of search. The hierarchy can also be set up to have branches for non-graphic data, contours, shotpoint data, elevation/depth data, well logs, etc.

Grids are also a logical basic organizational structure for data bases. Synercom calls each grid a facet, which is another name for a map sheet. Given an *x* and *y* location they can rapidly specify a facet, or a given facet can quickly retrieve the range of *x* and *y* values within the facet.[5] Polygonal retrieval allows users to define an area of interest within a global polygon, and then all of the facets defining data within that polygon are pulled out.

Hexagons form a basic organizational structure that is topologically more efficient than grids. Figure 10-2 illustrates the base and expanded aggregate of this type of structure. This has been named the Lucasian Graphic Data Base after the developer Dean Lucas.[6] This method of representing an N-dimensional surface so that a computer can easily work within the data distributed on the surface is called GBT. GBT stands for Generalized Balanced Ternary (ternary refers to being based on the number three). GBT is an extension of the one-dimensional system known as balanced ternary.[7]

GBT is not only a method for representing space (geographic locations on earth's surface), but also a sophisticated addressing scheme that allows rapid access to the representation. In addition there is an algebraic system that operates on the addressing scheme to allow rapid searching for a specific hexagonal unit. Simply stated, this structure allows a computer to examine the general content of a data set without looking at the detail. An algorithm can then determine at a high level if finer information is needed. GBT permits layered accessing of finer and finer data until a single hexagonal unit and all of the graphics and non-graphics (Figure 10-3) information associated with that unit are reached.[7]

The basic concept is the same as grid structural organization units, described earlier; however, there is a single GBT address in Lucasian graphics data base, as compared to dual *x* and *y* locations in a conventional Cartesian data base. This allows Lucasian systems to operate at higher access rates over a larger data base.

In fact, the latitude and longitude of each millisecond of arc covering the entire surface of the earth can be stored in one 64-bit

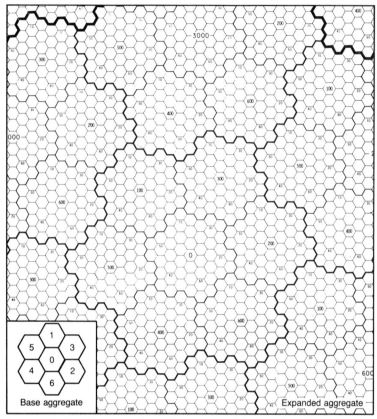

Figure 10-2. This illustrates the GBT structure of the Lucasian graphic data base. Each individual hexagon represents 1 millisecond of arc. Note there is only a single address needed for locating each main hexagon, compared to a dual x and y address needed to locate a point on a conventional Cartesian data storage structure. (Courtesy Interactive Systems Corp.)

octal word. (Octal refers to the 8-digit numbering system that is easier for computers to use than our standard decimal numbering system because it is a power of 2, on or off.) There are 20 of these octal words in each 64-bit word, or 7^{20} unique locations defined in a single computer word.

Relational data base management is a phrase that is often used to describe how different attributes, like spatial and textual material, can be related to a structural organizational unit. The concept is based on having the actual content of data within records arranged into simple tables. Relational DBM is virtually an indexing system, and, as in most scientific areas, relational DBM has its own language.

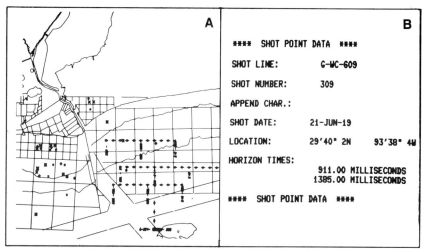

Figure 10-3. Displays from two CRT screens used to integrate an exploration data base. This shows that both textual and graphic data can be utilized in these computerized data systems. A graphically illustrates seismic line locations and lease boundaries. B shows the back up text, which describes a specific shot point from the map. (Courtesy Digicon Geophysical Corp.)

The key definition to understanding relational DBM is that a *relation* is simply a table. The relation name is known as a *map*. A column in the relation (table) is a *field* occurrence or an *attribute*. A row in the table is a *record* occurrence or a *tuple*. *Selection* is to separate a subset of records (rows) within a relation. *Projection* is taking a subset of fields (columns) within a record. *Joining* creates new relations (tables) from two or more existing relations, based on common field content.[6]

The software packages INGRES was developed at the University of California at Berkeley as a relational data base management system. It places all data in a series of tables or relations. There is a fully integrated data dictionary and the data manipulation language is much like English. This is the type of system that can be used to relate data sets directly to a basic structural organizational unit. The system also maintains a system catalog, which can be updated to allow flexibility in inputing new data types and used to set controls to ensure data integrity. The tables can also be used to create an open-ended number and hierarchy of menus for data base manipulation. As this type of software system improves, it can be moved into hardware to further improve the efficiency when the data base gets very large.

Storage becomes one of the key considerations in structuring large data sets. When one realizes that it takes 1.5 billion bits (750 Megabytes) to store maps of the city of Houston,[5] the problems of attempting to build a worldwide exploration data base appear insurmountable.

Further, the *type* of data that is included in the data file makes a tremendous difference in the amount of storage space required. One solution is to store only key parameters (map interpretations and other data reductions) in the data base, the idea being that these are the data of common interest to other departments. This saves storing voluminous, unreduced exploration data like seismic sections. Another solution extends this by keeping large-volume data on magnetic tape for easy batch retrieval.

Electronic storage technology is improving rapidly enough that the mount of data that can be economically stored for electronic access is regularly doubling. Data base systems are available with real-time retrieval of data from up to four fixed or removable discs (160 MBytes to 675 MBytes each).[8] With a little planning, this much direct access memory will allow the solution of most exploration data base problems. If necessary, larger storage systems could download (transfer) subsets of the data base (projects defined by map boundaries) to a user terminal or workstation for local evaluation.

Storage technology may also get a boost from a new technology called optical disc storage. This technology uses a laser to burn through an opaque absorber in order to write (turn a bit on). The system only allows one write, but one 14-in. disc will store 2,000 Megabytes of data, or the equivalent of almost seven 300-Megabyte discs.[9] Figure 10-4 compares this amount of storage with standard disc and tape storage. A jukebox configuration of this storage medium provides virtually an unlimited digital storage capability.

EXPLORATION APPLICATIONS

There are many ways that a DBM system can be incorporated by explorationists. Presently, subsets of the systems described are being used independently for geographic, geophysical and geolog-

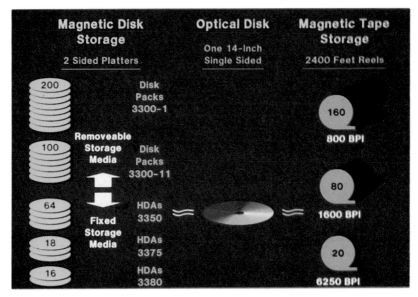

Figure 10-4. A comparison of storage capabilities on disc drives, magnetic tapes and the optical disc. (Courtesy Burroughs Corp.)

ical projects. Eventually, integrated systems will be developed to allow an exploration team to evaluate new areas for an exploration play, check for previous surveys, evaluate the lease situation, plan a new seismic acquisition survey, interactively process and interpret the seismic survey, and do the well log and reservoir evaluation. Of course, there is a lot of overlap in each of these different areas. The brief descriptions that follow describe a few of the ways these systems are presently being used in three exploration areas. There probably is not a currently marketed system that can perform all of these options at once; however, everything described is being demonstrated by one DBM system or another (1982).

Geographic

A relational geographic data base can be built that consists of culture (rivers, coastline, etc.), river depth and width, political and civil boundaries, lease blocks and ownership, shipping lanes, etc. The location of leases can be input in conventional or legal terms. Standard cartographic and line symbols are available. When maps

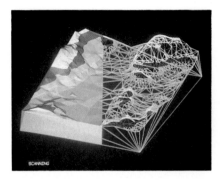

Figure 10-5. A triangularized topographic surface is processed through a hidden line algorithm and then displayed as a solid surface. This photograph shows the display when half of the surface has been filled in as a three-dimensional solid. (Courtesy Intergraph Corp.)

are scaled, the cartographic line symbols remain at the same scale. Figure 10-5 shows how a topographic contour map can be triangularized and viewed as a three-dimensional object, the hidden lines removed and the remaining surface displayed as a solid. In fact, user-responsive displays can be rapidly generated in a wide variety of views and orientations. The standard projections (Equator Mercator, Transverse Mercator, Lambert Conical, etc.) are available, and coordinate transformations can occur between different projects. In fact, independent coordinate systems, like that used in Nigeria, can be defined and integrated into world data base storage systems.

Geophysical

Figures 10-1 and 10-2 show how data base systems are being used to evaluate textual and graphic data like shotpoint and well locations. Some systems are sufficiently sophisticated that seismic sections can be evaluated, tied and interpreted on the screen. One geophysical area where the techniques described are being fairly widely used is computer contouring. Automatic contouring is considerably less expensive than hand drawn maps and the turnaround time is reduced dramatically. Line numbers, borders, title and title blocks can be plotted automatically. Although these maps need to be tied with other information, like regional structure and known geology, by an interpreter, they still can be of great benefit. This is especially true if there are a large number of maps that need to be generated, such as isochron and depth conversion maps.

Using the computer to do interactive wavelet processing on a seismic section opens a new world for interpreters. For example, a particular wavelet shape can be designated, graphically extracted and moved across the section to identify reflections with similar characteristics. This capability is especially useful in correlation of seismic and synthetic well log data. Many of the systems the author is aware of are set up so that transportable industry-accepted application software can be used with them.

Geological

Standard API symbols for mapping well descriptions are available. Figure 10-6 gives an example of how well log data can be edited by direct graphical manipulation. There are pre-defined algorithms that are on line to compute porosity, water saturation and lithology parameters. Even distorted paper logs can be digitized and then evaluated on a corrected CRT display. Once a well log relational data base is set up, the data base can be queried to get a display of all wells in an area with production between 8,000 and 12,000 feet.

Input/output

A hardcopy print or photograph of the results of a search are normally available in one form or another. However, the key to an interactive graphics tool is the softcopy display device.[10] One of the problems with explorationists using any of these input/output devices is that they are all different. This means that each device has a slightly different protocol, which frustrates non-computer scientists. Computer language failures have greatly slowed the growth of distributed systems in general. Figure 10-7 illustrates some research under progress at the University of Houston's Image Processing Laboratory to help solve this problem. The plan is to define an ideal display device controller that the explorationist will always talk to, no matter which terminal is being used.

Simplified procedures of using input/output devices will literally bring them into the analyst's office. There are presently systems that can be 6,000 ft away from the computer system and data storage center. Considerable intelligence can be placed locally in the terminal so that continuous pan, zoom and local dynamics are possible. As communication procedures continue to improve, the power of a major computer center can be placed in the field, or in a small remote division office.

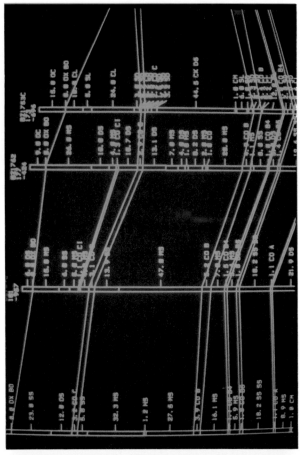

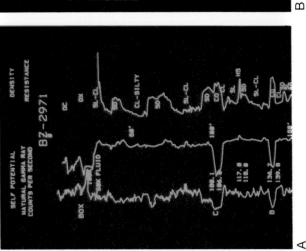

Figure 10-6. These photographs illustrate how interactive retrieval and mixing of different data sets aids interpretation. A compares a gamma ray and resistivity well log. B shows a small portion of a well log correlation for an overview evaluation. (Courtesy Synercom Technology, Inc.)

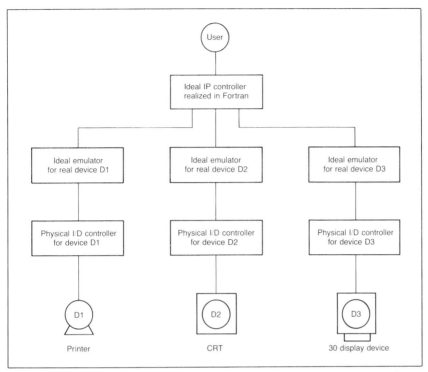

Figure 10-7. Each input/output display device is controlled by unique protocol. This diagram illustrates a project being undertaken to define the ideal controller so that a user could use any display device without having to know the specific characteristics of the device. (Courtesy University of Houston Image Processing Lab.)

SATELLITE DATA TRANSMISSION

Data bases and satellite transmission will not be tied directly together for several years. However, planning for the efficient use of DBM systems requires that a company evaluate the upcoming use of satellite data transmission over the next decade. Initially the use of satellites will be to batch download information overnight, because of the present long response times.[11] The biggest reason for the long response time is transmission rates, yet, these problems are already technically solved.[12] Therefore, the use of satellite transmission for distributed remote DBM is really a matter of politics and economics. Initial applications will include the capability to transmit data directly from the field to a processing center, to transmit data between processing centers, or to provide direct communication to field crews anywhere in the world.

Digicon and M/A-Com Linkabit Inc. of San Diego have reported a joint development and marketing arrangement to provide high speed, secure data transmission systems for the seismic exploration industry. Sea trials of a four-node system that transmits marine seismic tapes to a data processing center onshore is planned for the fourth quarter of this year. This system will use the Inmarsat satellite system and Marisat ship terminals currently tariffed at 56,000 bytes per second. The Digicon system contains 6,250 bpi tape drives, an encryption (encoding) description and a high-speed line error component.[13]

There are political and technical reasons why these communication systems have not been used to transmit geophysical data before. One of the biggest problems is illustrated in Figure 10-8. There is a big gap in INMARSAT's ground communication coverage that excludes Oklahoma City, Denver and Calgary, among others, from its transmission range. In order to transmit from the Gulf of Mexico to one of these oil centers, it is necessary to send the information back up to another satellite system. Also, industry wants to be able to transmit at 6 million bytes per second, which can happen now, but is expensive. Stabilization of the 7.5- to 12-m sending or receiving dish at sea is another critical technical problem;[12] however, there are stabilized platforms in use.

The political problems include legal regulations associated with transmitting from international waters. Also, although the system is inherently designed for transmitting 1.5 million bytes per second with "error free," high throughput performance, it is only tariffed for transmitting at a rate of 56,000 bytes per second.[13] There is also the intangible fear that something might destroy the satellite or that it will break down at a critical time.

SECURITY

The integrity of a computer data base or the satellite transmission of a portion of that data is of vital importance to those companies

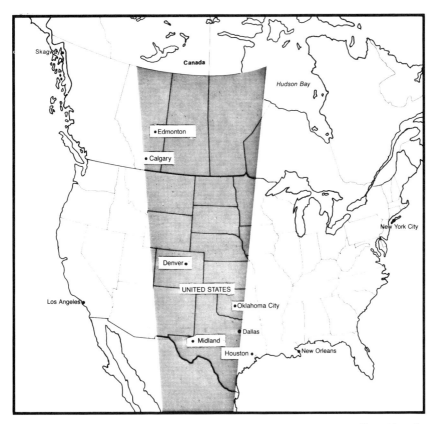

Figure 10-8. The ground communication coverage of the INMARSAT satellites. Note the large gap in coverage that excludes Oklahoma City, Denver and Calgary from receiving signals directly from INMARSAT. To transmit data to the areas within the gap, information must be re-sent through another satellite. This is just one of the problems that have kept satellite data transmission out of the oil patch. (Courtesy Digicon Geophysical Corp.)

that are beginning to use these new technologies. Computer crime must be taken into account.

Data bases can be secured by approving system users for a specific project. This security can be further tightened when a relational data base system is used, because user access can be even further limited within a project. But too much security can defeat the benefits of an interactive system. If someone wants to steal information, they will find a way and a self-justification to do so, regardless of the security. However, regularly changing passwords, requiring special authorization to edit master tapes and building in controls to allow monitoring of all access to the data base are the best security steps available.

For satellite transmission, there are cryption devices approved by the Bureau of National Standards that can be used to secure transmitted data. The ability to transmit 46 MB of data totally cryptic, with one of 2,400 codes that can be changed daily, is available today (1982).[12]

SUMMARY

One of the newest and thus least wide spread technologies in oil and gas exploration is the efficient use of computer data bases and satellite data transmission. There are all kinds of reasons why these procedures are good or not good. However, when it comes to the bottom line, they will have widespread use by explorationists when they are recognized as being cost effective technologies that aid in the management of the ever increasing volumes of scientific data available to industry. In fact, implementation of these systems promises to provide the same production increases that follows switching from a batch to an interactive processing procedure.

It seems that the decrease in time required to make critical exploration decisions will provide enough pay back alone to justify the initial investment of planning, hardware and software. Cecil C. Miller, senior geophysicist and operations manager of Tetra Tech's Energy Management Division, talks about his company's use of Cybernet to manage separate geological and geophysical data bases. "All people have a tendency to resist change. But in our circumstance change was forced, due to the magnitude of the task. You either use data processing or you don't get the job done."[14]

References

1. Townsend, D. W., "Computer Data Bases Aid Exploration," *Oil & Gas Journal,* pp. 144-159, July 2, 1979.
2. Nelson, H. R., Jr., "Modeling Resolves Complex Seismic Events," *World Oil,* pp. 61-70, Feb. 1, 1982.
3. Hodgson, R. N., *et al,* "Online Graphic Systems Speed Exploratory Analysis," *World Oil,* pp. 37-48, Feb. 15, 1982.
4. Drinnan, C. H., Synercom Technology, Inc., Houston, Texas, personal communication, 82.

5. Fox, T., Synercom Technology, Inc., Houston, Texas, personal communication, 1982.

6. Dillahunty, R. C., Digicon Geophysical Corp., Houston, Texas, personal communication, 1982.

7. Lucas, D. and Gibson, L., "Introduction to GBT," preprint, Interactive Systems Corporation, Denver, Colo., 1981.

8. Powers, M., Intergraph Corp., Houston, Texas, personal communication, 1982.

9. Ebrahim, S., Burroughs Corp., Westlake Village, Calif., personal communication, 1982.

10. Nelson, H. R., Jr.,, "Interactive Interpretation Comes of Age," *World Oil,* pp. 197-216, May 1982.

11. Smith, T. L., Digicon Geophysical, Houston, Texas, personal communication, 1982.

12. Basso, L. D., Macomnet, Inc., Houston, Texas, personal communication, 1982.

13. "Digicon, Inc.," Houston Business Journal, Section 3, May 3, 1982.

14. "Computer Helps Increase Productivity of Geoscientists," *Cybernet News.* No. 96, pp. 4-6, First Quarter 1982.

CHAPTER 11

Industry/University
Exploration Training

The current shortage of well-trained explorationists is the largest problem the oil and gas exploration industry has to face in the 1980s. While many scientists are being attracted from related fields, it takes years to educate them in the specific techniques utilized in hydrocarbon exploration. As a result, tremendous competition has been generated for those with the best brains and experience. This chapter reviews how the industry/university liaison has developed into an entity that can provide both the funding and the tools or techniques necessary for the proper training of new explorationists.

The level of scientific training offered by U.S. universities in recent years has fallen far short of its potential for several inter-related reasons: inadequate funding, lack of proper staffing and equipment and a shortage of high-level students entering post-graduate work. However, a close liaison between industry and academia could result in the alleviation of some of the problems, as it has in a few instances across the U.S. already.

Following is a discussion of the current scientific educational problem in this country as it specifically relates to exploration geophysics. Included is a review of ongoing industry-supported projects with a close look at the University of Houston's Allied Geophysical Laboratories. Additional suggestions are offered as to how other educational innovations could further solve this country's scientific training gap.

THE PROBLEMS

Numerous university graduate students who historically would have earned Ph.D degrees for teaching or research are switching to more lucrative careers in business, law, medicine, and engineering.[1] Although most oil companies have significantly reduced their recruiting efforts in 1983, exploration geophysics has not seen the job market tighten to the same degree that academia and many other professions have; and there is still a strong demand for well-trained explorationists. This demand is fueled by the fact that there continued to be a problem in the depth and overall quality of training that exploration scientists are getting in colleges today. Basically, few well-trained explorationists are being graduated.

Quality Shortage

The most serious portion of this problem is that the brighter students with a BS degreee in geophysics/geology or an advanced degree in a somewhat related field are being "bought" away by industry prior to their obtaining further education. (This is primarily because the recent demand for explorationists is actually a manifestation of the demand for oil.) However, although these students are often very intelligent, it is an exception for them to have obtained as firm a grasp of the mathematics, physics, geology, electrical engineering, computer science and geophysics that comes with the exertion required by a good graduate school program. The result is that while the number of explorationists increases, the percentage of well-founded, technically competent scientists is decreasing. Some oil companies obviously meet their short-term manpower needs in this manner, but such brain "buying" is not providing good foundation for continued, high-level exploration research and problem solving.

With the industrial dependence on highly trained professionals, it is important that industry correspondingly recognize the benefits of a long-term approach to personnel needs. This includes recognizing "that a mindless bidding war for these professionals would be destructive for everyone, and that...recruiters have an obligation to help universities assure the quality and expand their output of graduates in the sciences and engineering," says Dr. J. B. Slaughter, Director of the National Science Foundation.[2]

Another paradox is that "there are too many Ph.D. candidates and not enough quality," says W. G. Bowen, president of Princeton University.[1] This is a factor that will definitely affect future energy exploration research and development. As Bowen points out, "over the long-term we may face the possibility that the quality of teaching and research will diminish and entire fields of knowledge may be weakened."

The decline in the number of superior students attending graduate school has been dramatic. This slump cuts across the spectrum of academic fields, including those areas that have traditionally provided energy explorationists. Lewis Solomon of the Higher Education Research Institute of UCLA has documented this from surveys.[1] He points out that in 1964 about 75% of top-quarter college graduates who continued their education chose studies in the arts and sciences, while only 20% went into law, medical, or business school. In contrast, in 1969 more than half of the top graduates chose professional schools and only a third chose the arts and sciences.

As a specific example, comparing 1964 to 1981, Harvard University went from 77.2% to 30.8% of the seniors who graduated with highest honors going on to graduate school in the arts and sciences.[1] And the reason for this drop is obvious. There is so much difference between the starting salaries in industry and in academe in many of the engineering and scientific disciplines, that the lifetime yield of a person with a doctoral degree and a tenured position on a university faculty can never financially catch up with the financial yield of one who went into industry after an undergraduate degree.[2]

It is important that industry do its part to recognize and reverse this trend. Dr. Slaughter has pointed out that basic research was 14% of total U.S. research and development in 1980, the highest level in 15 years. This suggests that industry *does* recognize that long-term economic health depends substantially on the generation of new knowledge.[2] However, this new knowledge comes with the quality, and not the quantity of researchers working on a problem.

Along this line, it is interesting that the total number of graduate students has not decreased significantly, even though the better students are not continuing their studies. The National Research Council in Washington reports that the total number of students earning doctorates has only declined to 31,319 in 1981 from a high point of 33,756 in 1973.[1]

One major shift in U.S. educational systems is the number of international students being educated here today. The University of Houston, which serves a very culturally mixed community, has an enrollment which is 10% international students. This trend is not really that uncommon for universities across the United States, and perhaps it will have a positive impact on those universities that will be affected by the demographically projected 23% decrease in potential undergraduate students from 1978 to 1997. In fact, while the enrollment of U.S. students may decrease, the number of international students trained at U.S. universities will probably continue to rise.

Professor Shortage

One possible reason that this large number of graduate students is not meeting industry needs, is that there are so many experienced professors leaving academia to go into industry. A survey by the American Council on Education found that about 10% of the faculty positions in U.S. engineering schools were vacant in 1980, and computer science departments had openings as high as 16%.[1] Part of this is due to increased student loads in engineering and science. Professors are left with overtaxed teaching loads and laboratories with outdated equipment and instruments. This situation is so bad, in fact, that it has prompted John A. McDonald of the University of Houston's Allied Geophysical Laboratories to repeatedly point out to industry sponsors that the biggest challenge faced by universities is not to raise money for research, or to attract qualified graduate students, but to compete with industry for *qualified* professors and support staff.

It is hard to attract and keep quality personnel in university positions under the fiscal constraints that go with these jobs. Largely because of this, many university positions have been filled on a temporary basis by graduate students, and this is unsatisfactory from many points of view. One problem is the amount of teaching time taken away from professors for the training and retraining of students for staff responsibilities.

FUNDING RESEARCH/EDUCATION

U.S. universities are currently entering an era of change in re-
gard to program funding, as the current U.S. government administration is reviewing traditional federal funding of education
as part of its overall effort to trim federal spending. The Reagan
administration, in fact, is calling for more private sector funding of
education, and the bottom line is that higher education will lose
$6.5 billion between 1981 and 1984 due to federal spending
reductions.[3]

It must be remembered, however, as decisions are being made
about educational funding that the current problems faced by universities are closely allied to the problems facing U.S. industry
today. These problems include: inadequate transfer of research
results into practice, aging physical plants and equipment, ineffi-
cient energy usage, shortages of highly trained technical personnel, insufficient investment in long-term research and the diver-
sion of resources to satisfy regulatory requirements.[2] This being the
case, it appears that decisions affecting higher education will have
an impact on industry and vice versa. In short, decisions about
educational funding today will have a long-term impact on the
economic health of this nation. Stating this idea another way,
George Keyworth, director of the Office of Science and Technology
Policy and the President's science advisor, has pointed out that
science policy is not made in a vacuum. Science policy, he says, "is
an exercise in priority setting and decision making that must be
carried out in the context of other national policies such as those
concerning national security, international relations, energy, social
services and the economy. For example, science policy, without
considering economic policy, is irrelevant."[4]

Budget Specifics

In comparison with other budgets proposed for the 1983 fiscal
year, basic scientific research fares well. The amount of $5.8-billion
is a 12% increase over the actual 1981 fiscal year budget. However,
it is 5.5% lower than the real dollar value of the 1980 fiscal year
budget.[4]

One of the basic beliefs of the present administration is that applied research is a private sector responsibility. The Council for Financial Aid to Education recently reported that voluntary support for higher education rose by an estimated 11.3% in 1980-81 to a total of $4.2-billion.[5] Much of the pure research that the National Science Foundation (NSF) has been funding will continue, and at close to the same rate. However, real dollar values are down and industry does need to make more substantial investments in long-term research and education.

Exploration Funding

The status of university research and education funding sources as they are tied to exploration geophysics is best summarized by abstracting a survey of North American universities conducted by the Society of Exploration Geophysicists Research Committee in 1980 (Table 11-1). Despite some serious problems with the survey, it contains some very interesting information. Because of the intensive manpower effort required to keep the survey updated it is already incomplete. Other serious problems have resulted in the fact that the data will probably never be officially published. For example, none of the three universities that the author has been closely associated with returned their surveys. The University of Utah, Southern Methodist University and the University of Houston all have well-known geophysics programs in their own spheres, but none are included in the survey in question.

Table 11-1 is taken from the last item on this survey, which requested a list of areas of research interest. This question included a breakdown of the number of researchers, amount of financial support, sources of financial support, number of professional employees, number of students and available equipment. The table reproduced here only lists those areas of research that are either directly related to exploration geophysics or are listed as being supported by an oil exploration company. The $2.5 million reported by 25 different universities doing work in exploration geophysics averages out to about $250,000 per school per year. After salaries, indirect costs and fringe benefits (insurance, etc.) this does not leave an adequate balance for teaching and research in the cost-intensive world of seismic crews,[6] seismic processing[7] and interactive computer graphics.[8] The research income reported on this survey can be further broken down into government-only sources (20%), industry-only sources (18%), and combination industry/government projects (62%).

The Industrial Associates Program at several universities is one of the longer running procedures for attracting money from industry to aid education. There are several universities that have this type of program including Oregon State University, Scripps Institute of Oceanography, The University of Texas Marine Science Institute and Woods Hole. For the most part, sponsors of these projects provide no direction in the research, but support each of the projects with about $15,000 to $50,000 per year.

One of the major reasons for industry supporting these programs is to be able to evaluate the marine sparker and seismic data as soon as it becomes available. The author visited the Scripps program 1975 for the specific purpose of evaluating the sparker and single channel data that had been collected by the Scripps vessels in the Andaman Sea. In new prospect areas where there has not been a regional or detailed seismic survey, this data is often the only key to subsurface geology.

Although there is not usually direct contact with the students by sponsors, sponsorship also provides the benefit of having a direct liaison with the professors who supervise the work. Often pure research, as opposed to applied research, is being carried out under this type of a grant. This type of support can be viewed as an example of how industry is fulfilling a responsibility to society. However, more often pure research is funded through government agencies like the NSF. An example is the NSF funding of $4.5 million per year for COCORP, the Cornell Cooperative Reflection Program.

Research consortia provide a vehicle that industry can use to more easily direct applied university research. Normally this type of organization will have a very detailed charter to study something of specific interest to the oil companies. With the rapid expansion of exploration, here are often not enough in-house scientists in research development (R&D) to evaluate all of the new technologies that are influencing industry. However, this does not mean that companies will join every outside project that is proposed. W. G. Clement, Director of Research at Cities Service Co., points out that there must be limits. Although industry should support out-

(text continued on page 263)

Table 11-1
Summary of SEG Research Committee Survey on Universities with Active Research Projects in Exploration Geophysics, 1980

Name of University	Departments	Research area	R	$	Source of funds	P	St	Equipment available
U of British Columbia	Geop/Astrop	Time series/inversion	2	33	NSERC	2	2	Computer, Digital data
U of British Columbia	Geop/Astrop	Seismology/Tectonophysics	2	60	Industry, NSERC, DEMR	2	3	6-phone dig. marine sys; 2-channel Sonobouy sys, Geo Tech MCR-600, MER-800
U of British Columbia	Geop/Astrop	Instrumentation	1	20	NSERC	1	1	6-element telem. array; A/D conv. sys; FM-tape-rec. seismographs (5)
U of Calgary	Geol/Geop	Seismic stratigraphy	1	—	HBOG	—	1	DFS III, UNIVAC
U of Calgary	Geol/Geop	Radiometrics	1	—	HBOG	—	1	Helicopter-mounted, high-resolution
U of Calgary	Geol/Geop	Electromagnetics	1	—	HBOG	—	1	Gamma-Ray spectrometer, Analog scale model
U of Calgary	Geol/Geop	Gravity	1	—	Chevron	—	1	Worden Gravimeter
Colo. Sch. of Mines	Geophysics	Seismic exploration	6	500	Industry and Gov.	4	40	24-Chan DFSIII, 48-Chan DFS V, P/S vibroseis, TIMAP computer

Table 11-1 continued

Name of University	Departments	Research area	R	$	Source of funds	P	St	Equipment available
Colo. Sch. of Mines	Geophysics	Geophysical modeling theor.	4	200	Industry	0	10	CYBER 170/7; DEC LAB-11; TEK 4081, 4025, 4006 and 4016
U of Connecticut	Geol/Geop	Shallow marine seismic	1	8	NRC	1	1	Air gun/recording equipment for work on lakes and inlets
Dalhousie U	Geology	Marine seismology	1	8	NSERC	1	1	Basic profiling
Dalhousie U	Geology	Nearshore marine surveys	1	15	NSERC/EMR	–	–	EG&G sparker system, Varian magnotometer, ORE 3.5 KHz system
U of Iowa	Geology	Exploration geophysics	1	–	SEG	–	4	–
U of Delaware	Geology	Seismic studies, Continental margins	1	31	NSF, Lamont-Doherty	1	1	Bolt airguns, Hydrophones, Raytheon PGR, 6-Chan. camera recorder
U of Delaware	Geology	Seismic reflection, Baltimore Canyon	1	–	Delaware Geological Survey	1	0	Bolt hydrophones, airguns; Raytheon PGR, 6-Chan. camera recorder
U of Georgia	Geology	Economic geology	5	–	NSF, Industry	–	15	–
U of Georgia	Geology	Marine geology	3	–	NSF	–	5	–

R = No. of researchers
$ = Thousands of dollars in financial support
P = No. of professional employees
St = No. of students

Table 11-1 continued

Name of University	Departments	Research area	R	$	Source of funds	P	St	Equipment available
U of Santa Cruz	Geology	Economic geology	1	170	NSF, Amoco, Mobil, Shell	1	7	Single, multichannel reflectors, Union + multi-beam bathymetric source
U of Kansas	Geol/Geop	Seismic detection of underground voids	1	12	Kansas Geological Survey	1	1	12 Channel I/O Mini-Sosie DHR 1632
U of Kansas	Geol/Geop	Shallow seismic exploration	2	25	Kansas Geological Survey	1	1	12 Channel, 2 Wackers, recording van, cable truck
U of Kentucky	Geology	Applied seismology/gravity	1	158	NFS, Dept of Transportation, Amoco, U of K	Y	6	Worden, 3 seismographs, 5-station seismic array, Talos digitizer
Louisiana Tech U	Geosciences	Petroleum geology/gravity	1	–	Private Companies	–	–	– –
McGill U	Mining	Seismic interpretation	2	10	Canadian Gov.	0	2	Computer facilities
Michigan State U	Geology	Seismology	1	15	NSF	0	4	Gulf 49-to-21 trace recording system
Michigan Tech U	Geology	Seismotectonics-Seismicity	1	142	NRC	1	6	3 seismic systems, 3 portarecorder systems, 3 telemetry systems
Montana Tech U	Geophysics	Seismic	1	–	–	–	2	DFS III
U of Southwestern LA	Geology	Geophysical/Geothermal	1	124	DOE	2	2	Magnetometer, seismic data

Table 11-1 continued

Name of University	Departments	Research area	R	$	Source of funds	P	St	Equipment available
U of New Brunswick	Geology	Develop vibrator source	1	4	EMR	1	–	Electronic equip to drive and monitor vibrators
U of New Brunswick	Geology	Interpretation of NB seismic data	–			–	1	Over 100 line miles of data on magnetic tape
State U of N.Y.	Geoscience	Field geophysics	1	75	DOE	3	3	Temperature log, Gravimeter
State U of N.Y.	Geoscience	Marine geophysics	1	75	NSF	–	–	–
U of Oklahoma	Geol/Geop	Engineering seismology	1	–	Gulf R&D	–	3	SIE RS-4AC, Soiltest R-60 and associated hardware and software
U of Pittsburgh	Geology	Geophysical studies of the Blue Ridge	1	–	–	1	0	Geometrics GS-816
U of Pittsburgh	Geology	Theoretical models of seismic atten.	1	–	–	1	0	Pittsburgh
Portland State Univ	Earth Sci.	Stratigraphy of Columbia River basalts	1	–	Dept of Geol. & Mining Industries, State of Oregon	1	4	Gamma Counter System
Portland State Univ	Earth Sci.	Stratigraphy	1	25	Petro Co	1	3	Field equipment, sediment analysis equipment
Stanford U	Geophysics	Seismic data processing	2	400	Industry and Government	2	10	Minicomputer

R = No. of researchers
$ = Thousands of dollars in financial support
P = No. of professional employees
St = No. of students

Table 11-1 continued

Name of University	Departments	Research area	R	$	Source of funds	P	St	Equipment available
Stanford U	Geophysics	Rock physics	1	200	Industry and Government	2	5	Ultrasonic & sonic velocity, attenuation and hydraulic permeability
Texas A & M	Geophysics	Exploration seismology	1	50	Wes, NSF, Oil Co	1	2	DDS 630 with field Summer, DDS 620, SIE RS-4
Texas A & M	Geophysics	Seismic attenuation	1	120	Consortium of Oil Co.	1	3	seismic-wave lab (Rockwell Intl.) data analysis facilities
Wright State U	Geology	Seismic mapping of buried river valleys	3	5	Exxon	2	1	Digital data system, seismic rig and Mobile B-34 drill, Exxon processing
Wright State U	Geology	Seismic reflection and coal	1	30	Amoco, SSC	2	8	Amoco field equipment and processing center, SSC processing center
Wright State U	Geology	Seismic reflection and coal	2	25	US B of Mines	1	0	Denver office of U.S. Bureau of Mines Equipment

R = No. of researchers
$ = Thousands of dollars in financial support

P = No. of professional employees
St = No. of students

side R&D as part of corporate responsibility to society, there will not be support of a project if there is not an industry scientist to monitor the project.[9] There will be, of course, more support for projects that are attacking applied research problems of interest to sponsors. This support comes not only in the form of money, but also by means of visiting scientists, discussions with visiting sponsors, field data sets, access to company facilities, etc.

There are many different industry-sponsored research consortia around the United States. The first industrial consortia was formed by Dr. Jon Claerbout at Stanford University, in 1973, just before the oil embargo. This project is known as the SEP, which stands for the Stanford Exploration Project. There is no permanent university staff associated with this project. It is carried out under the direction of Dr. Claerbout, about a dozen graduate students and visiting scientists. Some of the scientists that have spent a year or so working at the SEP on leave from industry include: F. Muir, Chevron Oilfield Research Co.; L. Rocca, professor at Politecnico Electronica in Milan, Italy, and R. H. Stolt, Conoco Exploration Resources Group.[10] Research has emphasized a seismic migration technique based on the finite difference approach.

The next, best-known research consortium is at the University of Houston. The activities of the Seismic Acoustics Laboratory[11] (SAL) have been discussed in some detail in this book. Table 11-2 is a list of sponsors of the SAL as of May 1982. Figure 11-1 breaks down the membership as of May 1982 according to U.S. and international sponsors. Figure 11-2 illustrates the relationship between oil companies, seismic contractors or another membership category labeled "various," which refers to companies such as computer vendors.

The SAL is one of five research laboratories within the University of Houston's Allied Geophysical Laboratories (AGL). The research emphasis in SAL is theoretical and numerical modeling of field reflection seismology. The major research emphasis in the AGL is to study three-dimensional (3D) seismic techniques from field acquisition through processing and interpretation.

One of AGL's five labs, the Keck Research Computation Laboratory (RCL) provides service to other laboratories on a VAX 11/780 computer with a seismic processing package on it. The RCL is also doing research in vector programming on a CDC Cyber-205 vector computer. Income comes from services and grants.

Table 11-2
Consortium Members Supporting the Seismic Acoustics
Laboratory (University of Houston), May 1982

Amoco Production Co.	ICI Petroleum Services Ltd.
Aramco	Japan National
Arco Oil and Gas	Marathon Oil Co.
BP International Ltd.	Mobil R & D
Chevron Oil Field Research	Norsk Hydro
Cities Service Co.	Pennzoil Co.
Conoco Inc.	Petrobras
Control Data Corp.	Petty-Ray Geophysical
Digicon Geophysical Corp.	Phillips Petroleum Co.
Exxon Production Research	Prakla-Seismos G.m.b.H.
Fairfield Industries	Seiscom Delta, Inc.
Geco	Seismograph Service Corp.
Geophysical Development Corp.	Shell Development Co.
Geophysical Service, Inc.	Societe National Elf Aquitaine
Geophysical Systems Corp.	Statoil
Geoquest International, Inc.	Sun Exploration Co.
Getty Oil Co.	Superior Oil Co.
Gulf Research & Dev. Co.	Tenneco Oil Co.
Horizon Exploration	Texaco, Inc.
Hunt Oil Co.	Union Oil of California
IBM	Western Geophysical Co.

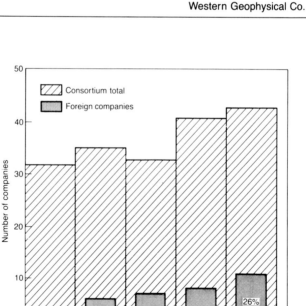

Figure 11-1. Membership breakdown of the University of Houston's Seismic Acoustics Laboratory as of May 1982 according to U.S. and international affiliation.

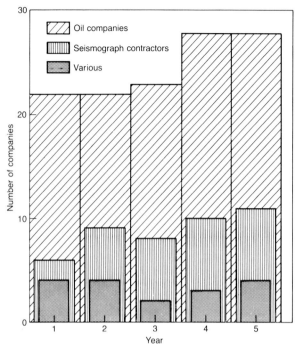

Figure 11-2. Membership breakdown of the University of Houston's Seismic Acoustics Laboratory as of May 1982 according to the designated industry sectors. The "various" category includes equipment manufacturers and vendors.

Another AGL member, the Cullen Image Processing Laboratory (IPL) is studying display techniques for placing seismic data on computer graphics terminals, interactive interpretation techniques and display and manipulation techniques for work with 3D volumes of seismic data. Funding is from a consortium of oil and computer graphics companies. The IPL has several pieces of advanced display hardware that are available to each of the labs in the AGL. This includes an Adage 4145 vector refresh graphics system with the raster segment generator,[12] an E&S PS-300,[12] a DeAnza IP-8500 image processing system,[12] and the Genisco SpaceGraph, a computer-controlled, true 3D display device.[13]

The Field Research Laboratory (FRL) of the AGL, will investigate new ways to acquire seismic data in the field. Income for this project is from government and industry grants.

The fifth laboratory, the Well Logging laboratory (WLL), is wholly within the University of Houston's Department of Electrical Engineering; whereas, the others are multidisciplinary, under equal direction of the College of Engineering and the College of Natural Sciences. The WLL is investigating improvements in well logging instrumentation. Its income is derived from a consortium of 16 oil companies.

What now constitutes the AGL has grown from one lab to five interconnected research labs since 1976. Further, 15 students have obtained graduate degrees with AGL support and all are working in energy-related industries.[14]

Another project that is sponsored by a consortium of most of the major oil companies and geophysical contractors is the MIDAS project at Columbia University. Midas is an inverted acronym, meaning Scattering And Diffraction, Inversion Migration. This project was originally started to evaluate and improve seismic evaluation techniques by using P & S waves (compressional and shear waves) simultaneously. There is an emphasis on using a modeling technique known as the finite element method. The facilities were orginally built with NSF funding, and the NSF is still supporting the project. There is a 3D physical modeling experimental facility that can use elastic media for looking at shear waves. Work in inversion has included the slant stack Tau-P method with amplitude as well as arrival time.[15]

The Colorado School of Mines (CSM) has a different approach. They have formed what is known as the Exploration Research Laboratory (ERL). The ERL is a contract research organization emphasizing field data acquisition, principally seismic. They are also doing time domain electromagnetic surveys tied to specific areas. One of the major projects was the Source Signature Study. This was a 1½-year project to evaluate the signature of various seismic sources. The idea is that a better definition of seismic sources will provide a basis for setting field parameters and processing parameters like signature deconvolution.[16] There are twenty two masters and three PhD students involved with the ERL who graduated in 1982.

The ERL also does site specific projects. For example, there is a fire-flood project to map shallow tar sand continuity and a high--resolution coal study near Vernal, Utah, as well as geothermal studies in the Snake River Plains and the Imperial Valley. The financial objective of these projects is to cover the costs. Sometimes they are cheaper than industry projects, especially if all of the processing steps are taken into account. The computer facilities at CSM consist of a CDC Cyber-720 computer that came as part of a $5.2-million grant to the geophysics department from the Keck Foundation. There is also a TIMAP computer for preprocessing. There has not been much of a cut in government contracts to the CSM, but the general economy is reducing support from several sponsors. This affects research and also academics at the school, because of the expensive overhead on the Cyber computer. One solution that is being applied to this problem is to sell excess computer time non-competitively to the Denver seismic community.[16] This can create a problem, however, if the university computer, supported by some state money, is selling computer time at a much lower price that is standard commercially.

There are several other research consortia that are studying areas of direct interest to exploration geophysics. Dr. S. B. Smithson at the University of Wyoming has a project to study ways of "seeing" through volcanics. Colorado State University has just started a project entitled Computations in Petroleum, which has over ten sponsors and is researching some applications of vector processors in the world of oil exploration. Dr. D. M. Johnson at the University of Washington is just starting a three-year project to study the rock properties of fractures using downhole tools to study crosshole elastic wave propagation (1982). A recent attempt to develop a cooperative project which innovatively would have used two boats to study U.S. Gulf Coast sediments failed because of the recession. All such projects obviously do not succeed.

Several schools that the author is aware of have recently purchased advanced seismic processing systems. These schools include Virginia Polytechnical Institute, the University of Wyoming, The University of Texas, The University of Houston and the University of Bahia in Brazil. Golden Geophysical, a group separate and yet close to and available to Colorado School of Mines students, has obtained three VAX-based minicomputer seismic processing systems (1983). There have also been other donations that are expected to have an impact on educating explorationists. For instance, Evans and Sutherland has donated some thirty-five PS-300 units, advanced line drawing or vector refresh graphics systems, to several universities. This includes two specifically for geophysical work—one to the University of Houston and one to the University of Texas at Austin.

One of the most ambitious university expansions currently taking place is at the University of Oklahoma in Norman, Okla. Effective this year there is a new Geoscience College with schools of geology, geophysics, meteorology, and a Department of Geography. The new energy center is from a gift of $30 million from Bill Saxton, an independent oilman. The university is increasing support and 27 fully-funded, tenured track faculty positions are planned for by 1985, up from 15. The goal is excellence, and an emphasis is planned in the energy areas.[17] The 1982 recession, however, has hampered the execution of some of the plans.

NEEDED INNOVATIONS

It was top news across the nation early in 1982 when the presidents of Harvard, MIT, Standord, the University of California and Caltech held a private conference with their peers at a dozen high-tech firms.[18] The purpose of the meeting, held at Pajaro Dunes, was to contemplate the ramifications of academia's new found interest in collaborating with industry, particularly in biotechnology. Harvard University President Derek Bok called the conference "reassuring in that it readily established a consensus, shared by business, about the importance of maintaining academic values while acknowledging the possiblity of creating sound relationships."[19] This has direct application to industry/academia relations in the area of oil exploration.

The type of policy that needs to be kept in mind in evaluating the oil industry's relationship with academia is expressed in the following portion of the Pajaro Dunes conference statement: "Agreements should be constructed, for example, in ways that do not promote a secrecy that will harm the progress of science, impair the education of students, interfere with the choice by faculty members of the scientific questions or lines of inquiry they pursue, or divert the energies of faculty members from their primary obligations of teaching and research."[20] With these ideas in mind it is reasonable to see other companies follow the example of Exxon Educational

Foundation's $15-million program to support doctoral students and junior faculty in engineering.[2]

There are several examples of how industry is establishing major, long-term joint projects with academia. The Massachusetts General Hospital (MGH) has a contractual agreement with Hoechst AG, a German pharmaceutical firm, for nearly $70 million over the next 10 years.[21] MGH has agreed to grant Hoechst exclusive worldwide licenses to any patentable developments that emerge from company-sponsored research. Exxon Research and Engineering has established a ten-year, $7-million project with M.I.T. to investigate combustion, and Monsanto has established a twelve-year, $23-million venture with Harvard to study the biological evolution of organs. In late 1981, Mallinkrodt announced it will fund almost $4 million of research on hybridoma technology at Washington University in St. Louis.[2] There needs to be the same kinds of commitments by the oil industry to develop even newer and better technologies to solve the complicated problems of exploration geophysics.

Several meritable proposals that have application in industry support of research and education in exploration have been listed by Dr. J. B. Slaughter of NASA.[2] These include: (1) building a $50-million industrial initiative directed towards sustaining the nation's creative engineering base, (2) having industry lobby state legislators for increases in faculty positions and salaries in a specific discipline in the state school system, (3) channeling direct support to schools that are willing to increase their capacity for engineering education, (4) increasing support for company employees to pursue advanced degrees under cooperative programs with a university, and (5) loaning industry scientists to universities to serve as adjunct and visiting professors or researchers. It also seems reasonable that a company could define what is proprietary and then set up a free exchange of remaining ideas and equipment with a university to aid in training students and accomplishing industry tasks.

At the same time, universities need to take positive steps. This could include reducing the quantity of graduate students, while at the same time encouraging those of the highest quality. There also should be ways to reduce the economic pressures of a six-year graduate study program. It would be hard to justify paying a geophysical graduate student twice or three times what a graduate student in another area can receive; however, the economic pressures of present industry needs make it foolish to continue in graduate school on a standard stipend.

SUMMARY

As related here, industry growth and educational excellence have closely tied destinies. Steps have already been taken within the exploration world to bring about better scientific research and development through the joint efforts of academia and private enterprise. However, with the federal government's push to make R&D more of a private sector concern, such academia/industry liaison must continue to expand if the exploration industry is going to have the well-trained professionals that it needs in the years to come.

References

1. Butterfield, F., "Grad Schools Face Crises as Brightest Forgo Doctorate Degrees," *Houston Chronicle,* from New York Times News Service, Section 5, p. 1, Wednesday, April 17, 1982.
2. Slaugher, J. B.,"Science An Engineering Research: The View from Washington," *Grants Magazine,* V. 4, No. 4, Dec., 1981.
3. Magarrell, J., "U.S. Cuts Said to Cost Colleges $6.5-billion,"*The Chronicle of Higher Education,"* May 26, 1982.
4. Hitchins, B. H., "Reagan Science Policy: What Grant Administrators Should Know," memo from the Office of Federal Programs, Washington, D.C., Mar. 26, 1982.
5. Magarrel, J., "Gifts to Colleges Reach $4.2-billion," *The Chronicle of Higher Education,"* May 26, 1982.
6. Nelson, H. R., Jr., "Trends in Multichannel Seismic Recording Systems," *World Oil,* pp. 135-142, Nov. 1981.
7. Nelson, H. R., Jr., "New Vector Super Computers Promote Seismic Advancements," *World Oil,* pp. 155-160, Jan. 1982.
8. Nelson, H. R., Jr., "Interactive Graphics Enhance Seismic Data Display," *World Oil,* pp. 76-82, Mar. 1982.
9. Clement, W. G., Cities Service Corp., Tulsa, Okla., personal communication, 1982.
10. Claerbout, J. F., Stanford University, San Francisco, Calif., personal communication, 1982.